F-22 RAPTOR

F-22 RAPTOR

America's Next Lethal War Machine

Steve Pace

McGraw-Hill

New York   San Francisco   Washington, D.C.   Auckland   Bogotá
Caracas   Lisbon   London   Madrid   Mexico City   Milan
Montreal   New Delhi   San Juan   Singapore
Sydney   Tokyo   Toronto

Library of Congress Cataloging-in-Publication Data

Pace, Steve.
    F-22 raptor : America's next lethal war machine / Steve Pace.
        p.   cm.
    Includes index.
    ISBN 0-07-134271-0
    1. F-22 (Jet fighter plane)   I. Title.
TL685.3.P33   1999
623.7'464—dc21   99-17914
                                                          CIP

McGraw-Hill

A Division of The **McGraw·Hill** *Companies*

1 2 3 4 5 6 7 8 9 0   DOC/DOC   9 0 4 3 2 1 0 9

ISBN 0-07-134271-0

The sponsoring editor for this book was Shelley Carr, the editing supervisor was Caroline R. Levine, and the produciton supervisor was Pamela Pelton. This book was set in Utopia by North Market Street Graphics.

Printed and bound by R. R. Donnelley & Sons Company.

This book is printed on recycled, acid-free paper containing a minimum of 50% recycled, de-inked fiber.

In memory of Benjamin R. Rich, 1925–1995

CONTENTS

The McGraw-Hill Companies is pleased to present the **Walter Boyne Military Aircraft Series.** The series will feature comprehensive coverage, in words and photos, of the most important military aircraft of our time.

Profiles of aircraft critical to defense superiority in World War II, Korea, Vietnam, the Cold War, the Gulf Wars, and future theaters, detail the technology, engineering, design, missions, and people that give these aircraft their edge. Their origins, the competitions between manufacturers, the glitches and failures and type modifications are presented along with performance data, specifications, and inside stories.

To ensure that quality standards set for this series are met volume after volume, McGraw-Hill is immensely pleased to have Walter J. Boyne on board. In addition to his overall supervision of the series, Walter is contributing a Foreword to each volume that provides the scope and dimension of the featured aircraft.

Walter was selected as editor because of his international preeminence in the field of military aviation and particularly in aviation history. His consuming, lifelong interest in aerospace subjects is combined with an amazing memory for facts and a passion for research. His knowledge of the subject is enhanced by his personal acquaintance with many of the great pilots, designers, and business managers of the industry.

As a Command Pilot in the United States Air Force, Colonel Boyne flew more than 5000 hours in a score of different military and civil aircraft. After his retirement from the Air Force in 1974, he joined the Smithsonian Institution's National Air & Space Museum, where he became Acting Director in 1981 and Director in 1986. Among his accomplishments at the Museum were the conversion of Silver Hill from total disarray to the popular and well-maintained Paul Garber Facility, and the founding of the very successful *Air&Space/ Smithsonian* magazine. He was also responsible for the creation of NASM's large, glass-enclosed restaurant facility. After obtaining permission to install IMAX cameras on the Space Shuttle, he supervised the production of two IMAX films. In 1985, he began the formal process that will lead ultimately to the creation of a NASM restoration facility at Dulles Airport in Virginia.

Boyne's professional writing career began in 1962; since that time he has written more than 500 articles and 28 books, primarily on aviation subjects. He is one of the few authors to have had both fiction and nonfiction books on the *New York Times* best seller lists. His books include four novels, two books on the Gulf War, one book on art, and one on automobiles. His books have been published in Canada, Czechoslovakia, England, Germany, Italy, Japan, and Poland. Several have been made into documentary videos, with Boyne acting as host and narrator.

Boyne has acted as consultant to dozens of museums around the world. His clients also include aerospace firms, publishing houses, and television companies. Widely recognized as an expert on aviation and military subjects, he is frequently interviewed on major broadcast and cable networks, and is often asked by publishers to review manuscripts and recommend for or against publication.

Colonel Boyne will bring his expertise to bear on this series of books by selecting authors and titles, and working closely with the authors during the writing process. He will review completed manuscripts for content, context, and accuracy. His desire is to present well-written, accurate books that will come to be regarded as definitive in their field.

The Persian Gulf War demonstrated one revolution in military affairs and caused a second revolution in political thinking. Together, these two revolutions are the best possible argument for the procurement of an adequate number of Lockheed Martin Boeing F-22A Raptor fighter aircraft.

The first revolution was the demonstration of air power as it should be used—quickly, decisively, and with overwhelming force. The United Nations built up their forces over time, trained together in the theater, and then conducted one of the most brilliant and decisive air campaigns in history. Local air superiority was secured almost immediately, theater air superiority was secured within a few days, and total air dominance was established before a week had passed.

The second revolution, in political thinking, was in its way as dramatic as the demonstration of total dominance in air power. The people of the United States, whom Saddam Hussein had expected to be infected with the "Vietnam syndrome" and oppose the war, reacted to the experience of total victory in an unusual way. The first reaction was one of pride, that the United States had perfected technology capable of such brilliant feats of bombing as were seen, almost in real time, on television. The second reaction was one of pleasure, that so few American casualties had been incurred, and that so little collateral damage had been inflicted on the Iraqis.

From these two reactions a pattern of thinking emerged. First, the people of the United States wanted to win all future wars in the same manner: quickly, decisively, and with few American casualties. Second, they also wanted to win all future wars with as few enemy casualties as possible.

Now this is revolutionary thinking. Never in the past has a nation been concerned in advance about enemy casualties. It speaks well that there is a general consensus within the United States that future wars should be won—but be won with minimum casualties on either side.

The corollary to this desire, however, is the requirement to maintain not air superiority, as was so laboriously obtained over the skies of Germany during World War II, and so grudgingly obtained in Vietnam. Rather, what is required is air dominance, the creation of an Air Force that will upon the outbreak of war completely and immediately suppress the enemy's air forces and integrated air defenses.

Fortunately, the means to achieve this air dominance is at hand. If the United States has the courage and the will to purchase enough Lockheed Martin Boeing F-22 Raptors, and undertakes the sustained effort to train its forces in their use, the United States Air Force will be able to achieve air dominance anywhere in the world upon a few hours notice. A nation so blessed as to have the ability to create a superior aircraft like the F-22 surely must also be blessed with the wisdom and the courage to procure the aircraft in sufficient numbers.

Steve Pace's narrative reveals, in explicit detail, just why the F-22 is such a formidable weapon.

This is the premier volume in McGraw-Hill's new series of aviation history books, a series of historical references created to present the latest information about the world's most exciting and interesting aircraft. Most important, the series is meant to be enjoyed by experts and laypersons alike. Subsequent titles in this series will illustrate the colorful histories of such great aircraft as the World War II Boeing B-17 Flying Fortress and the Consolidated B-24 Liberator. It will also include modern aircraft such as the Boeing North American B-1B Lancer, the Northrop Grumman B-2A Spirit, the Lockheed Martin F-117 Nighthawk, the Northrop Grumman F-14 Tomcat, the Boeing F-15 Eagle and F/A-18 Hornet, and the Lockheed Martin F-16 Fighting Falcon.

The purpose of this book is to inform those who like military aviation—aficionados, buffs, experts, historians, and novices—of the progress being made on the F-22 Raptor design, development, and production programs. Within the pages of this book on the F-22, the reader will find out exactly how this awesome fighter aircraft came into being and where its tremendous prowess will take it.

Chapter 1 describes how the Advanced Tactical Fighter program got its start, then progressed into a unique set of fighter and engine requirements, before metamorphosing into the air dominance fighter of today. Chapter 2 covers the developmental aspects of the F-22 and describes how it challenged and defeated seven ATF competitors. Chapter 3 discusses how the ATF prototype YF-22A beat the ATF prototype YF-23A, and the sad subsequent demise of the U.S. Navy's proposed carrier-based ATF. Chapter 4 describes the many ups and downs of the ATF program from late 1990 through the summer of 1997. Chapter 5 illustrates the F-22's numerous structures and systems, including its armament, avionics (electronics), cockpit, and engine. Chapter 6 reveals how the Raptor excelled over the magnificent Boeing F-15 Eagle, and introduces the primary people in charge of the F-22's initial success. Chapter 7 indicates how many F-22s will be built (under present planning) and how the U.S. Air Force (USAF) plans to use them. Finally, Chap. 8 illustrates the part stealth has played first in the successes of the stealth fighter and the stealth bomber, and now how it contributes to the survivability of the F-22 Raptor.

A Note on the Evolution of the F-22 Raptor

Since 1913, Lockheed Martin Corporation (formed by the merger of the Lockheed Aircraft Corporation and Martin Marietta) has designed, developed, and produced a lengthy line of successful military combat aircraft. These include such outstanding aircraft as the P-38 Lightning of World War II, the F-80 Shooting Star of the Korean War, and the F-104

Starfighter of the Vietnam War. The F-80 and the F-104 were the products of Lockheed's fabled Skunk Works, as were the U-2 Dragon Lady, the SR-71 Blackbird, and the astonishing F-117 Nighthawk.

Lockheed also won the hard-fought Advanced Tactical Fighter (ATF) competition, which now, has metamorphosed into the important F-22 Raptor program.

Officially classified as an air dominance fighter, the Lockheed Martin/Boeing F-22A Raptor is intended to enhance the tactical capabilities of the USAF in general, and its Air Combat Command (ACC) in particular. It is being carefully developed to at first complement and then succeed the Boeing (formerly McDonnell Douglas) F-15C Eagle air superiority fighter aircraft. When the F-22 Raptor achieves its projected initial operational capability (IOC) in 2004, the C version of the F-15, operational since the early 1980s, will have been operational for more than 20 years. There is no doubt that the Raptor will successfully supersede the USAF's F-15C Eagle—the world's current air-dominating fighter aircraft.

Incredibly intelligent and pilot-friendly, matchless in overall performance and maneuverability, the F-22 Raptor is to be a very lethal warbird. In an ideal scenario, armed with its single 20-mm Vulcan cannon for close-up aerial combat and up to six radar-guided and two heat-seeking missiles for beyond visual range (BVR) work, a lone F-22 could theoretically take out 8, 9, or even 10 enemy fighters during a single combat mission.

During an air-to-ground sortie, armed with two 1000-lb class Boeing (formerly McDonnell Douglas) GBU-32 Joint Direct Attack Munition (JDAM) satellite-guided smart bombs, with a circular error probable (CEP) of less than 15 m (current), and about 6 m (projected), a lone Raptor could destroy two strategic targets from as far as 15 mi away. It has a super-cruise capability to fly supersonically [with a Mach number of more than Mn 1.0+ and as much as Mn 1.5] without using its afterburners. Such speed will take it far away from its destroyed targets in a matter of minutes. If more speed is needed, it can light its afterburners and escape at more than twice the speed of sound.

Acknowledgments

The author would like to gratefully acknowledge the many helpful contributors for their cooperation in the creation of this reference. These are as follows: Sam Grizzle, Jeff Rhodes, Ray Crockett, Lockheed Martin Aeronatical Systems; Denny Lombard, Lockheed Martin Skunk Works; Eric Hehs, Lockheed Martin Tactical Aircraft Systems; Ray Puffer, AFFTC/HO; Fred Johnsen, AFFTC/HO; John Haire, AFFTC/PA; Robert F. Dorr; Mike Tull, Elaine Anderson, The Boeing Company; Nancy Colaguori, Pratt & Whitney Large Military Engines; Richard Kennedy, General Electric Aircraft Engines; and Shelley Carr, Walter Boyne, and the McGraw-Hill Companies Professional Book Group.

Formulating the Advanced Tactical Fighter

The Soviet fighter threat has reached technological parity with us. We must not allow them, or anyone else, to dominate the future.

RICHARD B. CHENEY *Secretary of Defense*

Total and unyielding air supremacy is the number 1 requirement to achieve a complete victory against any well-equipped adversary in a modern war. The need to maintain complete air superiority is imperative. This need first became apparent during World War I, when, for the first time, aircraft were extensively used for all-out warfare.

By the time the United States entered World War II, numerous advances in U.S. military aviation—especially in fighter-type aircraft—had been realized. No longer were U.S. Army and U.S. Navy biplane fighters armed only with two small-bore (.30-caliber) machine guns. Instead, following a paradelike succession of airframe and powerplant advancements, the Army and Navy had acquired a number of monoplane fighters with as many as four large-bore (.50-caliber) machine guns.

These single-wing army and navy fighters of late 1941—the Grumman F4F Wildcat, Seversky P-35, Curtiss P-36 Hawk, Bell P-39 Airacobra, and Curtiss P-40 Warhawk—quickly proved to be inadequate. They were demonstrably inferior to Germany's Messerschmitt Bf 109 and Japan's Mitsubishi A6M Reisen (better known as the *Zero*).

Experience quickly dictated that the Army and Navy acquire a variety of much improved fighter planes, heavily armed with six to eight .50-caliber machine guns. These included the Chance Vought F4U Corsair, the Grumman F6F Hellcat, the Lockheed P-38 Lightning, the Republic P-47 Thunderbolt, the North American P-51 Mustang, and the Bell P-63 King Cobra. The F4F, P-39, and P-40 fighters had fought valiantly, but after 1942, the more advanced P-38, P-47, P-51, F4U, and F6F fighters excelled, allowing the United States to gain and maintain air superiority in all theaters of operation.

The lesson was obvious. To prevent World War III, the United States had to continue to produce matchless fighter aircraft, able to secure air superiority. The new fighters would come just as the jet age unfolded.

The first generation of post–World War II jet fighters included the Grumman F9F Panther, the McDonnell F2H Banshee, the Lockheed F-80 Shooting Star, and the Republic F-84 Thunderjet. These provided the training and logistic base necessary for the development of the second generation of swept-wing aircraft that would be able to exceed the speed of sound.

The North American XP-86 Sabre was originally designed with straight wings, but the acquisition of data on swept-wing aircraft from Germany resulted in a decision to give the wings a 35° sweep. When modified with swept wings, the USAF North American P-86 became the first production aircraft capable of breaking the sound barrier, although this could only be done in a dive.

The F-86 (the designation was changed from P for *pursuit* to F for *fighter* in 1948) went into combat against the Mikoyan Gurevich MiG-15 during the Korean War. The MiG was marginally superior in performance to the early Sabres, but the superior pilot training, aggressiveness, and skill of the American pilots more than made up the difference.

Although the exact kill ratio of MiGs to F-86s is still debated, a generally accepted number is 792 MiGs shot down at a cost of 78 F-86s. Thirty-nine pilots became aces in the F-86, including the USAF "Ace of Aces" of the Korean War, Captain Joseph McConnell, who had 16 victories.

Despite its great success, the F-86, like any other fighter, had to be succeeded by the improved "century series" types. These were successively more expensive and complex, and included the North American F-100, the McDonnell F-101 Voodoo, the Lockheed F-104 Starfighter, the Republic F-105 Thunderchief, and the Convair F-102 Delta Dagger and F-106 Delta Dart.

Yet by 1965, when the United States was about to enter the war in Southeast Asia, the U.S. forces had only two air superiority fighters. These were the excellent Chance Vought F-8 Crusader and the McDonnell (McDonnell Douglas after 1967) F-4 Phantom. Both aircraft carried air-to-air missiles, but the F-8 was equipped with four 20-mm cannons from the start while the Phantom did not carry an internal gun until the advent of the F-4E. (Gun packs could be attached to external fittings.)

The F-8 used its guns to great advantage in the dogfights with MiG-17s, -19s, and -21s, and achieved a much higher kill ratio than F-4s. All U.S. air-to-air missiles had been designed for use against bombers, and had to be carefully managed to be effective during combat with a fighter.

Out with the Old and In with the New

The Soviet Union also continued to build many new fighter prototypes, and one of the most impressive of these was a fighter-interceptor aircraft designated MiG-25 and code-named *Foxbat* by the North Atlantic Treaty Organization (NATO). This new air-superiority-type fighter featured two very powerful turbojet engines and a speed approaching Mach number 3 (Mn 3)—three times the speed of sound. It had been developed as an all-out interceptor to challenge U-2s and SR-71s, and to meet and defeat the proposed trisonic B-70 bomber that did not enter production.

As a part of an ongoing process, and to counter any challenge like that of the MiG-25, USAF officials had initiated its Fighter-Experimental (FX) program in 1966. This generated a heated debate on the appropriate size for a fighter, with the extremes ranging between a 33,000-lb fighter and a 60,000-lb fighter.

The long debate, and the experience gained in Southeast Asia, resulted in an intense competition between a number of U.S. airframe contractors. On December 23, 1969, McDonnell Douglas—builder of the F-4—was selected to build the FX. The FX was subsequently designated F-15 and named *Eagle*.

At Edwards Air Force Base, California, McDonnell Douglas chief test pilot Irving L. "Irv" Burrows made the first flight of the F-15A Eagle on July 27, 1972 (USAF serial no. 71-0280). Further flight testing of this and subsequent F-15A/B aircraft quickly demonstrated the amazing capabilities of the extremely advanced air superiority fighter. It proved to be the most maneuverable, powerful, and agile fighter-interceptor aircraft ever produced for the USAF Tactical Air Command or TAC (Air Combat Command or ACC after June 1, 1992).

Approximately the size and weight of a World War II B-25 Mitchell twin-engine bomber, the Mn 2.5+ F-15 instantly showed it could literally fly circles around any other fighter in the skies. With its unique higher engine thrust to airframe:powerplant weight ratio, it became the first airplane in the world to exceed the speed of sound while climbing straight up! At this writing, about 27 years later, the F-15 arguably remains the best fighter in the world. Yet with the advent of much improved fighters from other nations in the mid-1980s—particularly from the former Soviet Union, but also from Europe—the USAF began the process of selecting a successor to the F-15.

Air Superiority Fighter Rivalry

In the mid- to late 1980s, Russia put into service a pair of advanced fighter aircraft to counter American fighters, including the F-15, the F-14 Tomcat, the F-16 Fighting Falcon, and the F/A-18 Hornet.

Two important fighter aircraft from the Soviet Union—the Mikoyan Gurevich MiG-29 Fulcrum and the Sukhoi Su-27 Flanker—had been operational since early 1985 and mid-1988, respectively. In response, the USAF initiated a program in mid-1983 to create a new air superiority fighter for the 1990s and beyond. Intended to counter both existing and future Soviet fighters, the new aircraft was called the *Advanced Tactical Fighter* (ATF).

The USAF's Aeronautical Systems Division (ASD) at Wright-Patterson AFB, Dayton, Ohio, created its ATF System Program Office (SPO), and the ATF program was officially begun. ATF design concepts were solicited in September 1983. The ATF SPO awarded contracts valued at about $1 million each to seven airframe contractors: the Boeing Airplane Company, General Dynamics, Grumman Aerospace Corporation, Lockheed Corporation, McDonnell Douglas Corporation, Northrop Corporation, and Rockwell International, North American Aircraft. The respective ATF concepts had to be received by the ATF SPO on July 31, 1984.

Two powerplant contractors—General Electric and Pratt & Whitney, were selected to participate in the ATF program under a 50-month duration Joint Advanced Fighter Engine (JAFE) program whereby each firm received identical $202 million contracts in October 1983. One of these engines would ultimately provide the propulsion system for the winning ATF aircraft.

Advanced Tactical Fighter Requirements

The prospective ATF contractors had to integrate the best overall features of current and future technologies into their ATF proposals. The aircraft had to be capable of supersonic cruise and maneuver, have stealth characteristics, and require far fewer hours of maintenance per hours of flight time than any previous fighter. The winning ATF would be the one that achieved the best integration of these technologies into a well-balanced, cost-effective air superiority weapon system.

To initially supplement and ultimately replace a formidable fighter such as the F-15 Eagle, the ATF System Program Office (SPO) had to formulate a concentrated set of precise requirements. In part, these included very high-speed integrated circuits or (VHSICs); active wing camber control; high-pressure hydraulic systems; nonflammable hydraulic systems; hydraulically actuated weapons racks; low-observable, or stealth, application; voice command and control; conformal, or blended, sensors; shared antennas; integrated flight control system and propulsion system controls; short takeoff and landing (STOL) capability; two-dimensional, thrust-vectoring, and thrust-reversing exhaust nozzles; artificial intelligence; advanced composite materials for airframe and skin structures; advanced data fusion and cockpit displays; integrated electronic warfare system or (INEWS); integrated communications-navigation-identification avionics (ICNIA); variable-speed, constant-frequency electrical generator; onboard oxygen-generating system; fiberoptic data transmission; and an advanced fighter engine.

Joint Advanced Fighter Engine Requirements

The old adage "an airplane can only be as good as its propulsion system" has always proved to be true. Without the proper powerplant-airframe combination, no airplane can be successful. In World War II, the altitude performance of Allison-powered North American P-51 Mustangs had been inadequate. When the Allisons were replaced by Rolls-Royce Merlin engines, the Mustang became a world beater—arguably the best piston-engine fighter of that war.

To create an adequate propulsion system for the ATF, the ATF SPO had to draft explicit qualifying factors. These included supersonic cruise capability (Mn 1.5+) without augmentation (afterburning); an 800-mi range; 35,000-lb thrust class power rating (full thrust, static at sea level); and the incorporation of two-dimensional thrust vectoring exhaust nozzles. Thrust reversers, once stipulated, were later deleted from the JAFE requirements. All of this was to be done at a unit cost of $40 million in 1985 dollars. (This was later reduced to $35 million.) The ATF engine competition was as intense and as important as the airframe competition.

Developmental Highlights

All seven airframe contractors submitted their respective ATF design concepts to the ATF SPO by July 31, 1984 as had been directed, and evaluations began in early August. Three months later, in November, the Milestone One System Acquisition Review Council (MOSARC) program review was held. This was the first major acquisition program evaluation and decision point of the Department of Defense (DoD) on the still very young ATF program.

On October 8, 1985, the USAF issued its formal Request for Proposal (RFP) document to the industry, soliciting contractor plans for the Demonstration and Validation (Dem/Val) phase of the ATF program. Technical proposals were due at the ATF SPO in 60 days, while cost and price proposals were due 75 days later. The officials in the ATF SPO received the responses and evaluated them during a 6-month source selection process. This narrowed down the number of seven ATF design concepts to five, eliminating Grumman and Rockwell.

The Dem/Val phase included evaluation of engineering data, wind tunnel tests, mockup inspections, subsystem tests, person-in-the-loop simulations, and maintenance demonstrations leading to detailed designs suitable for full-scale development (FSD) of the two competing ATF aircraft. These would ultimately compete against one another in a winner-take-all fly-off competition.

Another source selection was scheduled to follow the Dem/Val phase (including the fly-off) and result in the selection of a single contractor or contractor team to develop, flight-test, and produce the ATF. That choice would be made in the fall of 1986, with the projected first flights of both ATF contenders to occur in 1990.

Joining Forces

The astronomical development costs of the advanced technology integration processes made the risks of the competition so high that the manufacturers were forced to team up to share ATF development expenses, production, and profits. Two contractor teams resulted: Lockheed/Boeing/General Dynamics and Northrop/McDonnell Douglas. These teaming agreements included follow-up design, manufacture, test, and support of the ATF, with the understanding that the winning airframe contractor would be *prime* contractor, and the teammate(s) would be *principal* contractor(s).

On October 31, 1986, the ATF designs from Lockheed and Northrop were selected. They would be the prime contractors, while their team members would be the principal contractors. Each contractor team would build two flyable test aircraft along with an associated static (nonmoving) structural and fatigue test airframe. Each contractor team would also be required to fly its ATFs with both the General Electric and the Pratt & Whitney engines. This began a 50-month-long Dem/Val phase to end no later than December 31, 1990. At this time the model 1132 Lockheed/Boeing/General Dynamics ATF design was designated YF-22A, while the model N-14 Northrop/McDonnell Douglas ATF design was designated YF-23A. Simultaneously, the P&W model PW5000 ATF engine was designated YF119-PW-100 and the GE model GE37 ATF engine was designated YF120-GE-100.

Lockheed and Northrop each received a fixed-price contract of $818 million for the final Dem/Val phase, which included flight-test and evaluation (FT&E). At completion, one contractor team would advance to the FSD phase (Milestone Two) of the ATF program. The FSD [now engineering and manufacturing development (EMD)] phase was to last about 5 years and lead to the ATF's IOC in the late-1990s. The breakup of the Soviet Union, with the resulting reduction in U.S. defense spending, has resulted in both schedule delays and a reduction in procurement quantity for the ATF.

The USAF had hoped to procure at least 750 ATFs to supplement, then replace, its fleet of F-15s. Later ATF procurement plans reduced the total buy to 648, then 438. At this writing total ATF production has been reduced to 339 aircraft.

ATF Rollouts and First Flights

Appearing before its YF-22A rival, the first of two Northrop/McDonnell Douglas YF-23A ATF prototype aircraft (87-0800) was unveiled on June 22, 1990 at Edwards Air Force Base (EAFB). No new military aircraft had been first shown at Edwards before or after the Lockheed YF-12A was revealed in 1964. During the YF-23A's rollout ceremony, it was announced

Unofficially nicknamed *Black Widow II,* the first of two Northrop/McDonnell Douglas YF-23A ATF prototypes, the P&W YF119-powered one flies near Edwards AFB. The GE YF120-powered YF-23A reportedly exceeded Mn 1.6 while supercruising. *(USAF/HO.)*

that the new ATF aircraft was equipped with two P&W YF119-PW-100 engines; the number 2 aircraft would be outfitted with two GE YF120-GE-100 engines.

The YF-23A began a series of low- and medium-speed taxi runs to evaluate nose wheel steering, brakes, control feel, and other standard tests on July 7, 1990. On the following August 27, Northrop chief test pilot A. Paul Metz completed a successful 50-minute first flight of the YF-23A at EAFB. After taking off at 7:15 A.M. local time, the aircraft reached an altitude of 25,000 ft and a top speed of Mn 0.70 before landing at 8:05 A.M. Functional checks of basic subsystems were performed during its maiden flight. Following the flight, Metz said, "The airplane flies very clean, much cleaner than we expected. During the climbout I was using considerably less power than I expected, and the escorting aircraft were on afterburners just to stay with me—with my landing gear down. It appears to have a tremendous amount of excess thrust and that's exactly what we wanted with this airplane."

Two days later, the first of two Lockheed/Boeing/General Dynamics YF-22A ATF prototype aircraft (N22YF) was publicly displayed inside Lockheed's Site 10 facility at U.S. Air Force Plant 42, in Palmdale, California. This aircraft (called Prototype Air Vehicle 1 or PAV-1) was fitted with two GE YF120-GE-100 engines.

The number 2 YF-22A (N22YX, and later, 87-0701) appeared next, but the late arrival of its planned engines (two P&W YF119-PW-100s) slightly delayed its original rollout schedule. The number 1 YF-22A (nicknamed *Lightning II*) made its first flight on September 29, 1990 with Lockheed ATF chief test pilot Dave Ferguson at the controls. During the 18-minute flight from Palmdale to Edwards, Ferguson attained a speed of 288 mph (mi/h) and an altitude of 12,500 ft. After the relatively short flight, he said, "It was a very easy airplane to fly," adding, "I would be happy to put fuel in it and fly it this afternoon."

The second, GE-powered, YF-23A made its first flight on October 26, 1990 with Northrop test pilot Jim Sandberg at the controls. The flight lasted 44 minutes and the aircraft reached an altitude of 15,000 ft and a speed of 360 mph.

Under an $818 million contract from the USAF, Lockheed/Boeing/General Dynamics (later Lockheed Martin/Boeing) created two YF-22A ATF prototypes. On August 29, 1990, the first of two YF-22As was publicly unveiled for the first time at Lockheed's Site 10 facility at U.S. Air Force Plant 42 in Palmdale, California. *(Lockheed Martin Corporation.)*

Evolution of stealth. In this rare photograph taken in January 1991, a Lockheed Martin F-117A Stealth Fighter, the world's first operational aircraft designed to exploit low-observable or stealth technology, poses with the P&W YF119-powered YF-22A ATF prototype. While the former was designed on a two-dimensional computer program, the latter was created on a computer with three-dimensional capability. *(Lockheed Martin Corporation.)*

At dawn on December 11, 1990, pilots of the two YF-22As are completing their pre-flight checklists at Edwards AFB. Shortly after this photograph was taken, they took off and flew in formation for the first time. *(Lockheed Martin Corporation.)*

Four days later, on October 30, the P&W-powered YF-22A made its first flight from Palmdale to Edwards—a 14-minute test hop, flown by Lockheed test pilot Tom Morganfeld. The flight culminated after the aircraft had reached a speed of 360 mph and an altitude of 10,000 ft.

The competition was on in earnest; both teams had flown both of their prototypes, each one powered by a competing engine.

Worlds Apart: The YF-22A and YF-23A in Contrast

To meet the very same specifications that had been listed by ATF planners in September 1983, the seven ATF airframe contractors came up with fundamentally similar designs in terms of wing area, sweep, and general size. The Lockheed and Northrop designs were perhaps the most different of all, with the YF-23A appearing slim and almost sensuous in design, and the YF-22A appearing shorter, with an angular muscularity. The YF-22A's angularity provides a stealthy quality, and stems from its F-117 Stealth Fighter ancestry.

YF-22A

The Lockheed YF-22A features a single-seat cockpit covered by a large, high-visibility canopy. The two engines are mounted close together on the centerline of the 38-ft-long fuselage, which is 20 ft wide at its broadest point. The engines are fed by diamond-shaped intakes. There are three internal weapons bays: one on either side of the fuselage, and the other mounted ventrally on centerline. The airplane has two fixed, outward-canted vertical stabilizers with large-area trailing-edge rudders, and twin all-movable tailplanes that double as horizontal stabilizers and elevators (stabilators). Its all-movable, close-coupled stabilators mount in line with the very thin, semi-trapezoid-shaped wings and actually overlap

On November 28 and December 20, 1990, respectively, General Dynamics test pilot Jon Beesley and Lockheed test pilot Tom Morgenfeld fired nonexplosive AIM-9 Sidewinder and AIM-120 Slammer air-to-air guided missiles. Both pilots were flying YF-22A number 2 when they made these live missile firings. YF-22A number 2 is shown after the missile firing with USAF Lt. Col. Jay Jabour at the controls. Note the illustrations of two missiles on the exterior of the right engine's air intake. (Lockheed Martin Corporation.)

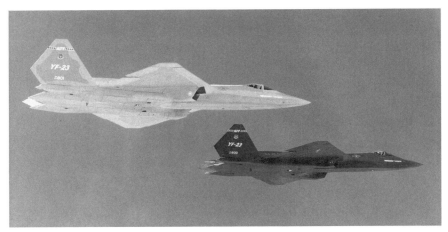

Both Northrop/McDonnell Douglas YF-23A ATF prototypes fly in formation in the summer of 1990. The YF-23As featured the all-moving V-tails. This unique feature helped reduce the aircraft's radar cross section while eliminating the unwanted mechanical devices and weight of conventional horizontal tailplanes. *(USAF/HO.)*

them. The wing's notched inboard trailing edge permits stabilator and flap clearance. The wing is swept back 48° at the leading edge, and swept forward about 15° at the trailing edge. The wings incorporate leading-edge flaps, inboard trailing-edge flaps, and outboard ailerons for lift and maneuverability. The YF-22A was equipped with two-dimensional, thrust-vectoring engine exhaust nozzles, and these may have been important in its final selection as the competition winner.

YF-23A

The Northrop YF-23A was one of the most beautiful fighter aircraft in history, its blended body and shielded engine intakes giving it a very sleek appearance and a clear relationship to the Northrop Grumman B-2A Spirit. There are no corners or right angles, and the surfaces have no creases or sharp folds. Like its counterpart, it also features a single-seat cockpit arrangement with engines mounted close to the centerline, with ventral air inlets. Engine installation is unusual. The intakes are placed under the wing (so as to ensure high angle-of-attack maneuvering capability) while the engines are canted upward into separate blended bodies. The long slender fuselage has chines not unlike those of the SR-71 or the Northrop YF-17.

The broad wing is triangular in shape and tapers into the fuselage. Its leading edge is swept back 40°, while the trailing edge is swept forward by the same amount. The YF-23 has a V-tail which works in roll, pitch, and yaw. Two large all-moving tailplanes are canted outward at 50°. The wing features leading edge flaps, inboard flaps, and ailerons that droop. The trailing-edge controls function normally—with ailerons providing roll

The YF-22A impressed the USAF with its vertical speed capability. The F-15C Eagle can exceed Mn 1.0 in a straight-up climb, and the F-22A Raptor will better that performance. *(Lockheed Martin Corporation.)*

control and flaps increasing lift—but they also serve as speed brakes and rudders. In its general appearance, the YF-23A appears to be optimized for high lift and low drag, and thus for long range and high speed.

Comparing the ATF Powerplants

General Electric and Pratt & Whitney took different approaches to meet the exact same set of ATF engine requirements that were put forth by the ATF SPO. In part, these are described below.

YF-119-PW-100

The Pratt & Whitney YF119 engine has a more conservative design than that of its competitor, and features significantly fewer and more durable components than previous fighter engines. It is able to operate at supersonic speeds for extended periods without augmentation; the actual time remains classified. YF119 (see Table 2-1) development started in 1983 and was selected over the YF120 to power the F-22 in April 1991.

YF120-GE-100

General Electric's YF120 engine was more radical than its competitor, featuring variable-cycle technology. This enabled the YF120 to operate like a conventional turbojet engine at supersonic speed, while demonstrating the characteristics of a more fuel-efficient turbofan engine at subsonic cruise speeds. The demonstrator engine, designated XF120, set a record for test duration and

This three-dimensional, computer-generated rendering shows the highly detailed ballistic vulnerability analysis model that was developed for the F-22A Raptor. Vulnerability analysis is conducted on an aircraft and its systems in order to determine their ability to withstand damage. *(Lockheed Martin Corporation.)*

TABLE 2-1 YF119-PW-100 Details

Type	Twin-spool, augmented low-bypass turbofan
Thrust	35,000-lb class
Combustor	Annular
Turbine	Axial flow/counterrotating

An excellent close-up view of the number two YF-22A as it rendezvous with a tanker. The first aerial refueling was accomplished on October 26, 1990. Note the excellent visibility afforded the pilot. *(Lockheed Martin Corporation.)*

Numerous models of the F-22's final configuration had to be built for wing tunnel evaluations and other purposes, This is an exact ⅟₂₀-scale model of the aircraft that was crafted by expert modelmakers. *(Lockheed Martin Corporation.)*

From December 10 to 17, 1990, YF-22A number 1 flew a series of high-angle-of-attack or high-alpha attitude tests. Antispin parachute and canister attached, the YF120-powered aircraft reached an AOA of 60° while it remained under full control. *(Lockheed Martin Corporation.)*

parameters measured at the USAF's Arnold Engineering Development Center or AEDC at Tullahoma, Tennessee. The scheduled 37-hour test period was the longest continuous turbine engine test in AEDC history; and, a record 875,000 measurements were taken during the test period.

The YF120 featured a dual-spool, vaneless, counter-rotating turbine. It also has improved materials and 40 percent fewer parts than GE's 29,000-lb thrust class F110-GE-129 fighter engine as used by the Block 50 F-16C Fighting Falcon aircraft.

YF120 development started in 1983 and was passed over in favor of the YF119 in April 1991. It is of interest that an updated version of the F120 is to be evaluated in both the Boeing X-32 and Lockheed Martin X-35 Joint Strike Fighter prototypes (see Table 2-2). Earlier, only the P&W F119 was being considered.

The YF-22A in Review

The Dem/Val phase of the ATF program began on October 31, 1986 and culminated with an intensive flight-test program at Edwards AFB in late 1990. In just over 3 months of flight testing, the two YF-22A prototypes demonstrated maximum Mach number, supercruise capability, high-angle-of-attack (high-alpha) maneuverability, aerial refueling, missile firings, and thrust vectoring. The vectored thrust is useful in both high angle-of-attack (AOA) maneuvers and for sustaining speed in high-speed turns.

The supercruise capability (supersonic flight without afterburner) was demonstrated on both aircraft using the different sets of YF119 and YF120 engines. The high-AOA work accomplished by YF-22A number 1 was impressive and gave the team high confidence in the F-22's stability and flight controls.

A total of 74 flights were flown on the two YF-22As for a total of 91.6 hours. After contract award in July 1991, another 39 flights totaling 61.6 hours were subsequently flown on the YF119-powered number 2 YF-22A in a follow-on Dem/Val flight-test effort.

The YF-22A and the F-22A are similar in shape, but there are a number of differences. The leading-edge sweep-back angle of the wings has been reduced 6° (from 48 to 42°); the cockpit canopy has been moved forward 7 in to improve over-the-nose visibility for the pilot, and the engine air inlets have been moved back 14 in to improve over-the-side visibility for the pilot; the shape of the wing trailing edges and the horizontal stabilizers and elevators (stabilators) have been changed to improve the aircraft's stealth characteristics, as well as for structural strength and aerodynamics refinement; also, the prominent vertical tails of the YF-22As have been reduced in size by about 20 percent.

As a result of the demanding schedule of the Dem/Val program, the team designed the vertical stabilizers of the YF-22A larger than necessary to avoid potential spin problems. When the spin problems never materialized,

TABLE 2-2 YF120-GE-100 Details

Type	Variable-cycle turbojet/turbofan
Thrust	35,000-lb class
Combustor	Annular
Turbine	Axial flow/counterrotating

On October 31, 1986 the Lockheed/Boeing/General Dynamics team became one of two teams selected to compete in the Dem/Val phase of the ATF program. Now some 12½ years later, three EMD F-22A Raptors are flying in the skies near Edwards AFB. *(Lockheed Martin Corporation.)*

the airframe designers were able to reduce the size of the vertical tails of the F-22A to make the aircraft more aerodynamically efficient by reducing drag and weight.

The first YF-22A was later brought to Lockheed Martin Aeronautical Systems (LMAS) in Marietta, Georgia, where it was used as an engineering mockup. It now resides at the Air Force Museum in Dayton, Ohio.

When F-22 production swings into high gear in the early 2000s, this artist rendering of LMAS's facility alongside Dobbins ARB will become a reality. The main assembly building is located at the upper right. *(Lockheed Martin Corporation.)*

The F-16 Fighting Falcon is a relatively small and light air combat fighter. A two-seat F-16 from Edwards is shown as it escorts Raptor 01 during its first flight. Their size comparison is interesting. *(Lockheed Martin Corporation.)*

Pratt & Whitney logo.
(Pratt & Whitney Large Military Engines.)

As mentioned above, the second YF-22A was used in the follow-on Dem/Val flight-test program in late 1991 and early 1992. Returning to Edwards after a test flight on April 25, 1992, it experienced a series of pitch oscillations. With the landing gear retracted, the aircraft hit the runway, slid, and burned. Although no longer flightworthy, the external damage was later repaired, and it was airlifted to the Rome Air Development Center at Griffiss AFB, New York, where it received representative F-22 wings and empennage and is still being used to validate aircraft antenna patterns. Final disposition of the second YF-22A has not yet been determined. (See Tables 2-3 and 2-4.)

TABLE 2-3 YF-22A Specifications

Propulsion system	Two 35,000-lb thrust class P&W YF119-PW-100 afterburning turbofan engines (PAV-1), or two 35,000-lb thrust class GE YF120-GE-100 afterburning turbofan engines (PAV-2)
Wingspan	43 ft, 0 in (13 m)
Wing area	830 sq ft
Length	64 ft, 2 in (19.6 m)
Height	17 ft, 8.9 in (5.4 m)
Empty weight	31,000 lb (estimated)
Gross weight	62,000 lb (estimated)
Service ceiling	65,000 ft (estimated)
Maximum speed	Mn 2.2+ (Mn 1.5+ in supercruise)

TABLE 2-4 YF-23A Specifications

Propulsion system	Two 35,000-lb thrust class P&W YF119-PW-100 afterburning turbofan engines (PAV-1), or two 35,000-lb thrust class GE YF120-GE-100 afterburning turbofan engines (PAV-2)
Wingspan	43 ft, 7 in (13.3 m)
Wing area	900 sq ft
Length	67 ft, 5 in (20.6 m)
Height	13 ft, 11 in (4.3 m)
Empty weight	29,000 lb (estimated)
Gross weight	62,000 lb (estimated)
Service ceiling	65,000 ft (estimated)
Maximum speed	Mn 2.2+ (Mn 1.5+ in supercruise)

The Winner Take All Fly-Off Competition

L ike the competition between the General Dynamics YF-16 Fighting Falcon and the Northrop YF-17 Cobra during the mid-1970s, the winner-take-all fly-off competition between the Lockheed YF-22A and the Northrop YF-23A was held on paper rather than as an all-out, unarmed air-to-air duel. By using computerized sensors and data acquisition, the USAF was able to quickly compare the figures generated by the two ATF contenders.

The YF-22A versus the YF-23A

Both ATF teams had created two excellent prototype fighter aircraft. Despite the YF-23A's earlier rollout, it soon appeared that the Lockheed/Boeing/General Dynamics team had taken the initiative. The first YF-22A initially achieved supercruise speed on November 3, 1990; the second, on December 27, 1990. Although classified, the YF-22A's supercruise speeds are probably above Mn 1.5.

The first YF-23A flew to a speed of Mn 1.43 at 42,000 ft on November 14, 1990 in its first demonstration of supercruise, and reportedly hit Mn 1.6+ in a later flight. The actual speed remains classified.

In a period of 7 flying days during December 10–17, 1990, the first YF-22A performed nine high-AOA test flights (14.9 hours), which included flight at 60° AOA. These high-alpha flights fully demonstrated the YF-22A's exceptional maneuverability at slow speeds and high pitch rates.

It took an exceptional fighter prototype aircraft to win out over the extraordinary Northrop/McDonnell Douglas YF-23A. The Lockheed Martin/Boeing YF-22A was that aircraft. As the late Ben Rich, second president of Lockheed Martin's famed Skunk Works, put it, "The F-22 is a performing miracle. It can fly supersonic without afterburners, and using a revolutionary Thrust Vector Control System, can fly at extreme angles of attack while changing directions at high speeds, thereby outperforming any other airplane in the world—all this with the stealth invisibility achieved by the F-117A." *(Lockheed Martin Corporation.)*

The YF-22A was designed at the Skunk Works in 1988. The Lockheed Corporation (now Lockheed Martin Corporation) agreement in late 1992 to acquire the Tactical Military Aircraft business of General Dynamics Corporation (GD) linked Lockheed's renowned advanced design and development skills with GD's widely recognized integration and production expertise. The YF-22A and F-16 Fighting Falcon symbolize the strength and technological capabilities of this corporate union. *(Lockheed Martin Corporation.)*

"I don't believe any other aircraft in the world could have done what we did with the YF-22," said General Dynamics (now Lockheed Martin Tactical Aircraft Systems) test pilot Jon Beesley. "We accomplished in one week what other programs set out to do in a year or more." He added, "It always did what I wanted it to do and never did anything that I didn't want it to do." In those nine test flights, flown by Beesley and USAF Major Mark Shack-

To adequately house two F119 engines and as many as eight AAMs internally, the YF-22A and its F-22A successor have relatively wide fuselages as shown in this head-on view of the ATF prototype. *(Lockheed Martin Corporation.)*

The fast, agile, stealthy F-22A will take over the air superiority role with the USAF starting in 2004, ensuring continued U.S. air dominance of the skies well into the next century. *(The Boeing Company.)*

The premier F-22A resembles a praying mantis as it rotates for its very first take-off. Production F-22As will not have instrumentation booms on their noses as Raptor 01 does here. *(Lockheed Martin Corporation.)*

elford, "We achieved our test objective, an unprecedented 60° angle of attack, and still had control power," Beesley said.

Earlier, on December 4, 1990, the second YF-22A successfully fired an inert AIM-9M Sidewinder air-to-air missile over the China Lake Naval Weapons Center in California. Then on December 20, 1990, the same aircraft successfully fired an inert AIM-120C "Slammer" air-to-air missile over the Pacific Missile Test Center off Point Mugu, California.

Surprisingly, the Northrop/McDonnell Douglas team did not conduct any missile firings or high-AOA maneuvers with their YF-23A aircraft. The reason for this remains unclear.

The P&W YF119-powered YF-22A banks left toward a moist Rogers Dry Lake (note water at lower right) at Edwards AFB in early 1992 during its second Dem/Val flight-test phase. Its exceptionally large all-titanium thrust vectoring exhaust nozzles are noteworthy. *(Lockheed Martin Corporation.)*

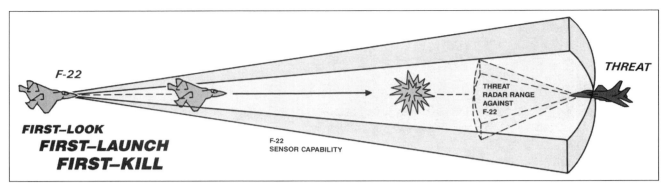

With its first-look, first-shoot, and first-kill capability, the F-22's radar covers far more area than any current adversary's radar. An enemy's aircraft would be spotted and destroyed before it ever saw the Raptor. *(Lockheed Martin Corporation.)*

Compare the proposed Navy Advanced Tactical Fighter (temporarily designated F-22C) with Raptor 01 as it climbs to 10,000 ft during its first flight on September 7, 1997. *(Lockheed Martin Corporation.)*

In a relatively short period of time, then, from their respective first flight dates in August and September of 1990 to the end of their flight-test programs in late 1990, the YF-22As flew at total of 74 times while the YF-23As flew a total of 50 times.

Earlier, on November 2, 1990, the USAF released its final RFP to end the Dem/Val phase and move on to the FSD (now EMD) phase. On that day, it was announced that ATF source selection evaluations would begin after December 31, 1990 and that the winner of the ATF competition would be selected by mid-1991 with an immediate announcement.

As it had been determined early on, the best ATF airframe-powerplant combination would go forth. With such a great deal at stake, both General Electric and Pratt & Whitney held their breath to see who would build the ATF powerplant, while the Lockheed- and Northrop-led ATF airframe teams did the same.

Choice Words

> If a distinguished scientist tells you it can't be done, he is probably wrong. If a techno-nerd at Lockheed says it can be achieved, he is probably right.
>
> ARTHUR C. CLARKE

After a hard-fought competition which had spanned nearly 8 years, the Secretary of the Air Force, Donald Rice, announced on April 23, 1991—about 2 months early—that the Lockheed/Boeing/General Dynamics team had won the ATF battle and would be awarded the EMD contract.

It was also decided that the P&W YF119-PW-100 ATF engine would be produced as the propulsion system for the F-22 production aircraft. In other words, it was the number two YF-22A (N22YX), powered by the P&W YF-119 engine, that would ultimately lead to the production of the Lockheed Martin/Boeing F-22A Raptor of today.

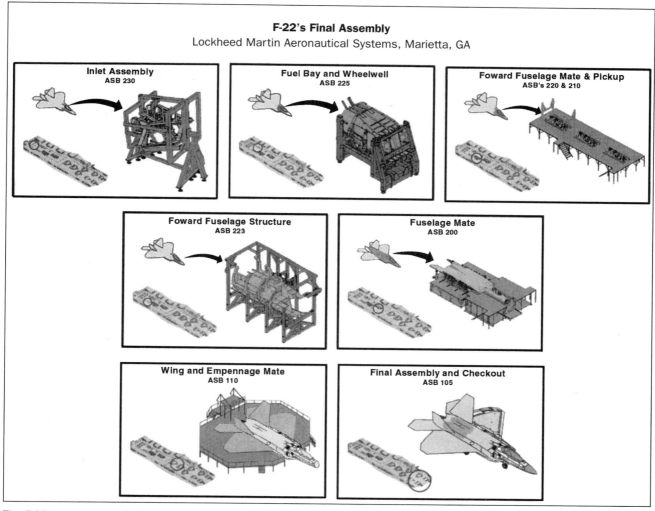

F-22's Final Assembly
Lockheed Martin Aeronautical Systems, Marietta, GA

The F-22's seven-step final assembly stops are pointed out in this illustration. *(Lockheed Martin Corporation.)*

The Navy Advanced Tactical Fighter

The U.S. Navy's (USN) best shipboard fighter is the Northrop Grumman (formerly Grumman) F-14 Tomcat. It is an aircraft carrier-based area- and point-defense fighter-interceptor, armed with a single 20-mm Vulcan cannon and as many as six long-range AIM-54 Phoenix radar-guided missiles. It can also carry a number of radar-guided AIM-7 Sparrow, heat-seeking AIM-9 Sidewinder, and radar-guided AIM-120 "Slammer" missiles in various armament packages. The first example of the Tomcat first flew on December 21, 1970.

The USN's next best shipboard fighter is the multi-role Boeing (formerly McDonnell Douglas) F/A-18 Hornet. It performs as both a light-attack bomber and an air superiority fighter/fighter-interceptor. First

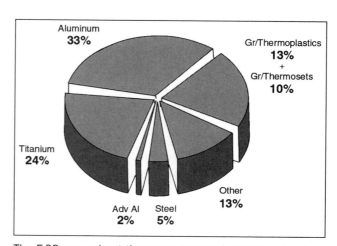

The F-22 uses about the same type and quantity of various materials as the YF-22A prototypes. *(Lockheed Martin Corporation.)*

The Raptor was designed with a three-dimensional computer program, unlike the F-117, which was designed with a two-dimensional one. As a result, the F-22 has a more sophisticated shape. *(Lockheed Martin Corporation.)*

flown in preproduction prototype form on November 18, 1978, the F/A-18 also has a single 20-mm Vulcan cannon and carries a wide assortment of bombs and missiles.

In 1986, during the early days of the Advanced Tactical Fighter program, the Tomcat was already 16 years old, and the Hornet was 8 years old. The USN began to look at its future fighter requirements. It was privy to the USAF's ATF program, and it sought to incorporate a navalized version of the ATF into its carrier fleets. This gave birth to the Navy Advanced Tactical Fighter or (NATF) program.

The USN thought a carrier-based version of the ATF would be the perfect replacement for its F-14 Tomcat series of fighters. The idea was to create a navalized ATF with strength-

With its two very advanced P&W turbofan engines, the Raptor can take on any adversary's fighter and win the battle. *(Lockheed Martin Corporation.)*

To ultimately replace the Northrop Grumman F-14 Tomcat, operational since 1974, the U.S. Navy considered procurement of a carrier-based, swing-wing version of the F-22 called the NATF. Instead, it opted for improved F-14s called *Super Tomcats* and improved F/A-18s called *Super Hornets*. Other than its variable geometry wings (a la the F-14), the NAFT featured a beefier landing gear and arresting gear package for carrier landings. In addition, its stabilators and its cockpit and canopy were of different configurations. *(Lockheed Martin Corporation.)*

AVIONICS OPERATIONAL REQUIREMENTS

PERFORMANCE

- **BASED ON ZONES OF OPERATIONAL INTEREST**
    1. **GENERAL SITUATIONAL AWARENESS**
    2. **TARGETS PRIORITIZATION BY ID AND/OR THREAT POTENTIAL**
    3. **ENGAGE OR AVOID DECISION**
    4. **DETECTION TO ALLOW DENIAL OF THREAT ADVANTAGE**
    5. **IMPLEMENTATION OF DEFENSIVE REACTIONS**

- **AZIMUTH AND ELEVATION COVERAGE VARY BASED ON EXPECTED THREAT ENCOUNTERS AND TRADE-OFFS OF SENSOR PERFORMANCE**
- **INFORMATION VARIES WITH EMISSION CONTROL MODE & AUTONOMOUS/ COOPERATIVE OPERATION**

AVAILABILITY/SUPPORTABILITY

- **OPERATIONAL AVAILABILITY DETERMINES:**
    - **MAINTENANCE-FREE OPERATING PERIOD**
    - **INTEGRATED ONBOARD DIAGNOSTICS REQUIREMENTS**
    - **TWO-LEVEL MAINTENANCE SYSTEM**

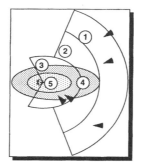

The avionics operational requirements for combat-ready F-22s is shown here. During Desert Storm, USAF F-15Cs downed more than 30 aircraft without any losses. Moreover, their mission-capable rate was higher than 85 percent; that is, they were ready to fly into combat more than 85 percent of the time. The F-22's mission-capable rate is to exceed 95 percent. *(Lockheed Martin Corporation.)*

This view from directly above shows off the Raptor's multihued light-to-medium-gray paint scheme. It will nearly disappear against blue or gray daytime skies when viewed from below. *(Lockheed Martin Corporation.)*

ened landing gear (for hard and short landings aboard carriers) and folding wings for reduced carrier stowage space.

Unfortunately, the NATF program was terminated in the early 1990s and the Navy developed its F-14D Super Tomcat and its F/A-18E/F Super Hornet aircraft for its immediate needs. However, as the Super Tomcat and Super Hornet aircraft grow increasingly older, the long-extinct NATF program could be revived as the Navy Air Dominance Fighter (NADF) program. A navalized version of the F-22 would meld well with the USN's upcoming Joint Strike Fighter (JSF). Nevertheless, this remains to be seen.

From ATF to ADF

Both the airframe and engine teams set to work immediately to create the world's best fighter aircraft. Even the ensuing buyouts and mergers which revolutionized the aerospace scene did not impair the smooth running of the ATF development program. (Lockheed acquired General Dynamics in Fort Worth, then merged with Martin Marietta to form Lockheed Martin. Boeing acquired Rockwell's North American aircraft interests and McDonnell Douglas.)

Approximately 9 years and 5 months had elapsed from October 31, 1986 to April 9, 1997, when the premier Lockheed Martin/Boeing F-22A Raptor was first shown to the public. During this near-10-year timeframe, the prototype YF-22A Advanced Tactical Fighter had been changed into the lethal F-22A Air Dominance Fighter.

Agonizing Reappraisals

By the time the Lockheed Martin/Boeing and Pratt & Whitney combination of airframe and powerplant had culminated in the form of the single-seat F-22A and the projected tandem-seat F-22B, world affairs had altered drastically. The Berlin Wall had been torn down, the Cold War had ended, and the Union of Soviet Socialist Republics (USSR) had disbanded. The Persian Gulf War had been easily won, primarily by an unprecedented showing of modern airpower. Defense spending was cut back by almost 40 percent over the next 5 years. Most military aircraft production programs were being either dramatically reduced or completely terminated.

Unfortunately, even though military aircraft production totals shrink, their program costs often continue to rise. In the case of the F-22, the original 750-plane requirement costing an estimated $26.2 billion was quickly reduced to 648 aircraft that was estimated to cost some $86.6 billion. After the Bottom Up Review, completed by the DoD in September 1993, the planned quantity of F-22s was reduced to 438 aircraft at an estimated cost of $71.6 billion. Then, in mid-May 1997, after the release of the Quadrennial Defense Review Report, the total F-22 production amount was reduced even further to 339 aircraft. In an effort to save funds, an F-22 production slowdown was required, which increased rather than decreased the single-unit price of each F-22. At this writing the cost of an F-22 now stands at about $90 million.

F-22 Production Program Slowdown

The original EMD contract called for the manufacture of seven single-seat F-22A and two tandem-seat F-22B aircraft with the first flight of EMD airplane number 1 (an F-22A) to take place in mid-1996. It also stipulated that the first full-production F-22A would fly by mid-1999, and that the first operational squadron would be active in the year 2003.

However, by February 24, 1995, when the USAF approved the final design of the F-22A aircraft, the first EMD F-22A had not flown yet, and the projected dates of the F-22A/B evolution had drastically slipped.

Considered the first-generation stealth aircraft, this artist's concept of an SR-71A Blackbird fully illustrates its wing-to-engine nacelles blending, fuselage chines, and inward-canted vertical tails, which all contribute to its stealth capabilities. *(Lockheed Martin Skunk Works.)*

With music, speeches, videos, and a laser light show, the premier EMD F-22A's public debut on April 9, 1997 was attended by some 2500 invited guests. General Richard Hawley, commander of the USAF's Air Combat Command, the ultimate user of the aircraft, announced the official name for the next-generation fighter: Raptor. "This is the day we officially name a remarkable—in fact a revolutionary—new multimission fighter," said Gen. Hawley. *(The Boeing Company.)*

VISTA, T-33, and the 757 Flying Test Bed: F-22 Support Aircraft

In an effort to expedite the time-consuming flight test schedules of the F-22A Raptor, the Lockheed Martin/ Boeing team employed three very different aircraft for assistance. These are the NF-16 VISTA, a Lockheed T-33, and the 757 Flying Test Bed aircraft.

VISTA

Flying a specially configured F-16 Fighting Falcon, test pilots completed tests on the first block of flight control laws for the F-22 in 1996, more than a year before the first flight of the actual aircraft.

The flight control laws (the complex set of computer instructions that keep a modern fighter aircraft flying) for the F-22 were programmed in the Variable Stability In-flight Simulator Test Aircraft (VISTA), a highly modified, one-of-a-kind F-16D (86-0048) that, through a sophisticated control system, can emulate the flight characteristics of another airplane in flight.

A total of 21 sorties totaling 26.8 hours were flown in the NF-16D (the official designation for the VISTA aircraft; with N meaning special test, permanent) in two test phases. The first test session was devoted to comparing the baseline flying qualities of the F-22 to proposed and potential changes in the aircraft's pitch and roll characteristics for landing, air refueling, and formation flying. The second phase focused on two aspects of F-22 flying qualities. The first aspect concerned how the control laws performed during an engine failure, and separately, two different failures of the hydraulic system, including a dual hydraulic failure that resulted in mechanical failure of one horizontal tail, one rudder, an aileron on one wing, and a flaperon on the other wing. The second aspect considered the effects of not accurately achieving the predictions of the F-22's aerodynamics and structural characteristics. The so-called parameter variation test flights allowed for relatively large changes to be made in the Raptor's stability and flight control power.

In smooth air, the various failures and parameter variations were almost indistinguishable from those of the baseline F-22. In more severe wind and turbulence, some differences could be noted, but the aircraft remained well behaved, and respectable landings could be made even with a severely degraded aircraft as a result of the simulated dual hydraulic failure. In the final analysis, the overall results of the NF-16D VISTA tests were excellent.

This head-on view of Raptor 01 during its rollout ceremony shows its deep, diamond-shaped fuselage to good advantage. Its very large engine air inlets are noteworthy. *(Lockheed Martin Corporation.)*

Lockheed T-33

In December 1997, one of Boeing's privately owned Lockheed T-33A T-Bird aircraft (N12416), usually used for Boeing's commercial jetliner flight-test and photographic chase duties, was suspended from the 80-ft-high ceiling of Boeing's F-22 Avionics Integration Laboratory in Seattle for radar cross-section—or radar profile—testing. It is being used for a calibrated airborne target in F-22 radar testing. Once installed in the range, the T-Bird was rotated and pitched through a wide range of angles to measure its full radar profile. To accommodate the T-33's weight (9300 lb), a special hoist-and-hanger mechanism was installed beneath the radar range's turntable. The T-33 has a telemetry package that transmits its position and velocity to test engineers at the F-22 AIL while "flying" against the F-22's AN/APG-77 radar. That type of data will help them verify the radar's performance. Radar testing against the T-33 began in May 1998 using a test radar located within Boeing's AIL.

The now-classic T-Bird was used extensively for many, many years as the USAF's primary jet-powered trainer.

757 Flying Test Bed

In October 1998, the F-22A's Flying Test Bed (FTB), a modified Boeing company-owned 757 jetliner (the first one built), was initially used by Boeing to integrate and flight-test the Raptor's highly integrated avionics suite. Boeing has the lead for testing the F-22's avionics system in the current EMD program.

The 757 FTB sports an F-22 forward fuselage section (built by LMAS in Marietta) installed on the 757's forward-pressure bulkhead. The structure houses the AN/APG-77 multimode active, electronically scanned array radar designed for the Raptor.

A second modification was the installation of a sensor wing on the crown of the 757's fuselage immediately behind the flight deck. Electronic warfare (EW) and communication-navigation-identification (CNI) sensors mount directly on the sensor wing, which is designed to simulate the sensor positioning found on the F-22's wings. The configuration provides high-fidelity data and allows the FTB to emulate the sensor capabilities of the F-22 in realistic, real-time operations.

The nose modification was completed in August 1997 at Boeing's Wichita, Kansas, facility, and inflight radar testing began shortly thereafter. Boeing completed the installation of the sensor wing in December 1998.

An artist's concept of the F-22 Flying Test Bed (FTB) also known as the 757 FTB or simply FTB, sporting an F-22 forward fuselage (nose) installed on the 757's forward-pressure bulkhead housing the Northrop Grumman AN/APG-77 radar. Immediately behind the 757's flight deck is the sensor wing on the crown of the fuselage. Mounted directly on the sensor wing are the electronic warfare or (EW) and communication, navigation, and Identification sensors. *(The Boeing Company.)*

A close-up view of the F-22 forward fuselage attached to the Boeing 757 FTB. The 757 FTB (N757A) is the first 757 built. Boeing installed the sensor wing in late 1998. *(The Boeing Company.)*

757 Flying Test Bed Configuration

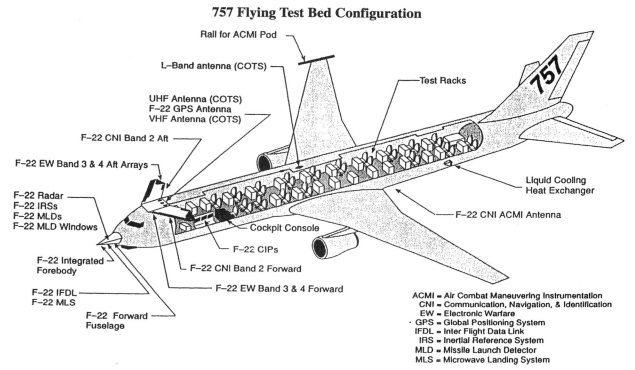

Rail for ACMI Pod

L–Band antenna (COTS)

UHF Antenna (COTS)
F–22 GPS Antenna
VHF Antenna (COTS)

F–22 CNI Band 2 Aft

F–22 EW Band 3 & 4 Aft Arrays

F–22 Radar
F–22 IRSs
F–22 MLDs
F–22 MLD Windows

F–22 Integrated
Forebody

F–22 IFDL
F–22 MLS

F–22 Forward
Fuselage

Cockpit Console

F–22 CIPs

F–22 CNI Band 2 Forward

F–22 EW Band 3 & 4 Forward

Test Racks

757

Liquid Cooling
Heat Exchanger

F–22 CNI ACMI Antenna

ACMI = Air Combat Maneuvering Instrumentation
CNI = Communication, Navigation, & Identification
EW = Electronic Warfare
GPS = Global Positioning System
IFDL = Inter Flight Data Link
IRS = Inertial Reference System
MLD = Missile Launch Detector
MLS = Microwave Landing System

The 757 FTB configuration shows the numerous F-22 avionics that are being tested. Test racks and seating for more than 25 technicians shown. *(Lockheed Martin Corporation.)*

Internal modifications to the twin-jet 757 include structural supports for the special nose and sensor wing structure and the installation of unique electrical power, liquid-cooling, and instrumentation systems. Avionics racks, test station racks, and seating for more than 25 technicians are located in the 757 ATB cabin.

The F-22B Takes a Back Seat

In the past, to facilitate the transition or pilots into new fighter aircraft, a small number of them are built with two seats and dual flight controls. In this way, by the time the pilots were ready to transition into the new single-seat fighter they had been assigned to fly, they had been fully familiarized with the aircraft and its flying characteristics. For example, the F-15D is a two-seat fighter-trainer aircraft for the single-seat F-15C Eagle. In the beginning, it was no different for the F-22. However, in an effort to further reduce the ever-rising F-22 development costs, the fighter-trainer version of the Raptor was dropped.

Then, on July 10, 1996, the F-22A/B airframe team received an official notification from the USAF that it had postponed its requirement for the design and development of the then-germinating two-seat F-22B aircraft. Therefore, the two planned EMD F-22Bs were replaced with two additional one-seat F-22As. Thus, all nine EMD F-22s will now be single-seat models.

Rollout Ceremony and First Flight of Raptor 01: The Spirit of America

The first EMD F-22A was almost completed by March 6, 1997, when it was moved from the final assembly area in Lockheed Martin Aeronautical System's B-1 building to the newly constructed B-22 engine noise attenuation facility, called a "hush house," where it underwent fueling operations and engine runs.

Little more than a month later, on April 9, sporting its patriotic Spirit of America nose art, the premier F-22A—marked "Raptor 01" on the outer sides of its two vertical tails, the first of nine EMD aircraft (91-0001)—was publicly unveiled in ceremonies at Lockheed Martin Aeronautical Systems facility in Marietta, Georgia. During the ceremony, the new fighter was christened with its official name: Raptor. (Raptors are birds of prey.)

As originally planned, the first of nine EMD F-22A Raptors was scheduled to take place on or before May 29, 1997. However, a number of minor yet significant gremlins attacked Raptor 01. Among these problems were aircraft braking and landing gear retraction/extension difficulties. It took about 3½ months to address and correct the difficulties. Finally, in late August, the aircraft was cleared for ground tests leading up to its first flight.

Earlier, on June 10, the Pratt & Whitney F119-PW-100 engine was granted its initial flight release. Before Raptor 01 could make its maiden flight, however, it had to complete the ground tests that included low-, medium-, and high-speed taxi tests. This series of taxi tests evaluated its nose landing gear wheel steering system, the braking system, and the operation of the arresting gear at 30, 60, and 110 knots. The instrumentation system on the aircraft was likewise thoroughly examined during these ground tests.

The long-awaited first flight of the first Raptor occurred on Sunday, September 7, 1997 at Dobbins Air Reserve Base (ARB) in Marietta, Georgia, with F-22A chief test pilot A. Paul Metz under its cockpit canopy. Liftoff came at 10:18 A.M. local time. Flying chase on the first flight was fellow contractor pilot Jon Beesley in an F-16 Fighting Falcon and Lt. Col. Steve Rainey, the first USAF pilot to fly an F-22A, in a second F-16 chase aircraft.

In preparation for the first takeoff, all three aircraft taxied onto the runway. The two F-16s took off first and started a slow 360° turn back toward the runway. Metz remained on the runway, making final instrumentation checks with the mission control room team.

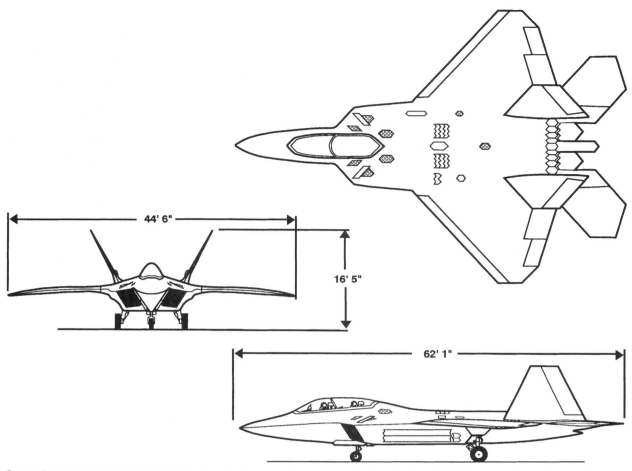

General arrangement drawing of the canceled two-seat Lockheed Martin/Boeing F-22B fighter trainer. Though it was to have a rear seat, its overall measurements remained identical to the single seat F-22A. Two EMD F-22Bs were to be built, but to save money and development time the USAF decided against them. *(Lockheed Martin Corporation.)*

Metz released the brakes, simultaneously easing the twin throttles to military power with his left hand. The P&W F119 engines spun up, and the F-22 started to roll down the runway. At about 140 knots, Metz eased back on the sidestick controller with his right hand. The aircraft rotated and lifted off. The landing gear remained down as the F-22A climbed to the north.

The most impressive feature of the first flight was the Raptor's rate of climb. Even with its gear down, the two F-16 chase aircraft found it difficult to keep up with the F-22. The two P&W F-119 engines produce a colossal amount of thrust, some 70,000 lb in afterburner. The F-22 was scheduled to climb out at about a 25° pitch angle in military power, but Metz had to raise the nose even higher several times to keep the F-22A's speed constant. The relatively steep climb angle was a function of the requirement to maintain constant velocity (speed) under a fixed engine power (thrust) setting.

Raptor 01 reached an altitude of 15,000 ft (2.84 mi) in less than 3 minutes. Once at that altitude, Metz leveled off and then cycled the F119s through a series of power changes. The engine afterburners were not used during the aircraft's initial flight, during which a maximum angle of attack of 14° was attained.

About midway through the near 1-hour-long test hop, Metz raised the landing gear and increased the Raptor's altitude to 20,000 ft, the maximum altitude for the flight. At 20,000 ft, he performed additional engine transients and evaluated low-speed cruise performance

As a Lockheed Martin flight line technician guides it ahead, the awesome size of the Raptor becomes obvious. When the Raptor becomes operational, its maximum takeoff weight will exceed 60,000 lb. *(Lockheed Martin Corporation.)*

before descending. On his way down, Metz flew formation on Beesley's F-16 to establish the F-22's handling qualities during relatively demanding piloting tasks.

The preplanned flight profile culminated with the landing gear again lowered for a pair of simulated landing approaches at 10,000 ft. Metz then made his final approach to Dobbins ARB. As the Raptor's main landing gear touched down, Metz aerobraked (held the F-22A's nose high) to slow the aircraft to about 100 kts before lowering its nose landing gear to the runway and applying the brakes. For this initial flight, he used the full length of the runway before the aircraft came to a full stop. The flight lasted 58 minutes from liftoff to touchdown at 11:16 A.M. During the flight, the F-22A attained a maximum speed of 250 kts and a maximum load of 3g [three times the force of (acceleration due to) gravity].

Another view of the premier EMD F-22A (AF 91-0001) as it taxis toward the main runway at Dobbins ARB. Operational F-22s will excel over the F-15 Eagle much as the F-15 excelled over the F-4 Phantom II. *(The Boeing Company.)*

Liftoff! Looking every bit like the bird of prey it's named after, the Raptor breaks ground and takes wing for the first time on September 7, 1997. In addition to greater lethality and survivability, the F-22 design calls for higher reliability, maintainability, and sortie (mission) generation rates than the F-15 it will replace. *(Lockheed Martin Corporation.)*

Metz had flown twice around a triangular route which had taken him about 40 mi north from Dobbins to an area near Rome, Georgia, and then southwest toward Alabama, and back to the vicinity of Dobbins. After the flight, Metz said: "The Raptor has wings," and added, "The test program will demonstrate that it has talons as well."

As of April 1997, Paul Metz had more than 6000 hours and more than 33 years of experience flying 72 aircraft types. Before joining LMAS, Metz was the Northrop chief test pilot on the Northrop/McDonnell Douglas YF-23A program. He was named LMAS chief test pilot for the F-22 in October 1992.

With its landing gear still extended, Raptor 01 performs a series of low-speed maneuvers to verify its handling characteristics. With its balance of increased speed and range, enhanced offensive and defensive avionics, and reduced observability, threats that the F-15 will no longer be able to counter will be defeated by the F-22. *(Lockheed Martin Corporation.)*

A two-seat F-16 Fighting Falcon (AF 78-0088) of the 412th Training Wing at Edwards AFB flies chase Raptor 01 over Georgia. The F-22's primary objective will be to establish absolute control of the skies through the conduct of counterair operations. *(Lockheed Martin Corporation.)*

With the sun coming from its right side, Raptor 01 shines brightly on its maiden flight. The first flight was preceded by a series of taxi tests. These tests were used to evaluate the Raptor's nose landing gear wheel steering, the braking system, and the operation of its arresting gear at 30, 60, 90, and 110 knots. The arresting gear is to be used in emergency landings. *(Lockheed Martin Corporation.)*

Raptor 01's second flight took place on September 14, 1997 with Lockheed Martin Tactical Aircraft Systems F-22 test pilot Jon Beesley at the controls. The flight, shortened by a telemetry problem, lasted 35 minutes. Beesley had worked on the ATF/F-22 program for 10 years and had accumulated about 20 hours in 13 flights in the YF-22A prototype aircraft.

Final assembly of the second EMD F-22A (Raptor 02) was completed on schedule, and the aircraft was rolled out of the 3.5-million-sq-ft main assembly building at LMAS' facility in Marietta on February 10, 1998. The aircraft was towed across the runway at adjoining Dobbins ARB, down the Lockheed Martin production flight line, and over to the F-22 engine test facility—the hush house, where it underwent fueling and fuel tank integrity checks. Once those operations were complete, the aircraft (4002) was towed across the ramp to the company's robotic paint facility, where it received its two-tone gray camouflage paint scheme. Then it was towed to the flight line to be prepared for its maiden flight.

Raptor 02 made its first flight 11 days ahead of schedule on June 29, 1998 with Metz at the helm. It was flown to an altitude of 20,000 ft at speeds of up to 280 mph (250 knots). Lt. Col. Steve Rainey flew chase in an F-16.

Metz flew the aircraft from Dobbins ARB, lifting off the runway at 140 knots with Raptor 02's F119 engines at military power (full power without afterburner). He performed maneuvers designed to demonstrate flying qualities, including bank-to-bank rolls, flight at varied engine power settings, and landing gear retraction and extension. The flight lasted 1 hour and 6 minutes.

Tom Burbage, the F-22 Team program office manager, said, "The first flight of the second F-22 is testimony to the viability and vitality of this program." He added, "We worked hard to incorporate the lessons learned on Raptor 01, and we succeeded. This airplane was brought to flight much more easily and efficiently than the first. We'll continue to learn and improve through the remaining seven EMD aircraft as we prepare to enter production next year [1999]."

F-22 Flight-Test Operations

The flight-test operations for the Air Dominance Fighter program fall under what is called the F-22 *Combined Test Force* (CTF), an integrated government/contractors-led test team that was formed for the preparation, planning, conduct, and reporting of the F-22's flight-test program.

This integrated test team is composed of personnel from many locations, including the Air Force Flight Test Center (AFFTC) at Edwards AFB, California; the Air Force Operational Test and Evaluation Center (AFOTEC) at Kirtland AFB, New Mexico; Air Combat Command (the ultimate user of the Raptor), at Langley AFB, Virginia; Pratt & Whitney; the F-22 SPO at Wright-Patterson AFB, Ohio; and the Lockheed Martin/Boeing team.

The various personnel and organizations functioning as the F-22 CTF are responsible for

- Estimating the scope of the air vehicle flight-test program
- Organizing the test team to accomplish assigned tasks
- Determining and obtaining sufficient resources (budget, schedule, material, facilities, and personnel) for successful accomplishment of the flight-test program
- Developing planning and documentation that adequately describes the flight test program
- Conducting the flight-test program in a safe, efficient, and effective manner
- Reporting the flight-test program status, accomplishments, significant problems, and results

Because of the geographic locations of the various organizations involved, the CTF at first functioned as a virtual colocated entity by using methods such as frequent face-to-face meetings and videoteleconferencing. Fully colocated operation of the F-22 CTF commenced with the delivery of the first EMD F-22 to Edwards AFB.

The F-22 CTF started with about 290 people and is to build to a maximum of 650 people in 2001. Initially the CTF was comprised of a 60/40 percent mix of contractor and USAF personnel. As testing progresses, the mix is projected to shift to 50/50 percent. The organization will be commanded by an USAF officer, with a contractor deputy. The internal organization is built around *integrated product teams* (IPTs), which produce the flight-test data on their respective products.

The *Airworthiness IPT* is permanent at Marietta, Georgia, and is responsible for taking the EMD F-22s from manufacturing through initial ground tests, flight-test airworthiness, and their ferry flights to Edwards AFB. The *Air Vehicle IPT* is responsible for all tests on the first three EMD aircraft, while the *Avionics IPT* was intended to do the same for the six EMD avionics test aircraft. All other participants support the IPTs, enabling the test pilots to receive their assignments from flight operations but work directly for the IPT when conducting flight tests.

Preparation and Planning Phase

The major objective of the F-22 CTF during this phase is to determine the various IPT requirements and to ensure that they are consistent with published plans and are fully traceable to contractual product specifications, or are required to measure the military utility of the F-22 Weapon System. From these requirements, detailed *Test Information Sheets* (TISs) are written, to verify the actual content of the test program. They identify supporting resources (instrumentation, data processing, personnel, facilities, equipment, etc.) and define documented methods and processes of operations.

Flight Test Requirements Working Groups

Flight Test Requirements Working Groups (FTRWGs) are set up to execute the test planning process. The FTRWGs' responsibilities and location were determined by the Lockheed Martin/Boeing assignment of product and/or technology design responsibility on the basis of the integrated product team (IPT) philosophy. This enhanced communications between the various product IPT personnel and the test IPT personnel, particularly in the early stages of test requirement identification.

The working groups are generally divided by disciplines. The groups had to decide exactly what had to be tested and who would be doing the tests. The working groups remain intact throughout the test program, and are responsible for the test conduct, data analysis, and reporting for their particular technical discipline.

Instrumentation, Data Processing, and Software

Each one of the nine F-22 Raptors to be built in the current EMD phase will be dedicated to flight test, and each one of these aircraft will be heavily instrumented to record flight-test data.

Unlike past aircraft development programs, the flight-test IPT was brought in at the very beginning of the F-22 program (EMD contract award). On other aircraft, the flight test was normally brought in after the aircraft was built and had to integrate flight-test instrumentation where it could find room to install it. On the F-22 then, flight-test IPT worked closely with the aircraft's designers, and the instrumentation incorporated in the original aircraft design was (and still is) installed during construction of the aircraft. In other words, the EMD F-22s flying at this writing are fully instrumented.

So with the planned instrumentation already installed as the first EMD F-22 entered final assembly in March 1997, flight-test IPT was able to start telemetering data to the Flight Test Control Room in Marietta, Georgia, which began the actual checkout of the data processing system.

A large orange-colored box with flight instrumentation flies in the EMD F-22's right-hand main weapons bay; armament test aircraft will use a different location. The box, called the *instrumentation data acquisitions package,* acquires data from more than 30 remote units scattered throughout the aircraft. The box contains a high-speed data recorder that retains all the flight data. It also encrypts and transmits selected parameters back to the mission control station on the ground via two antennas on the aircraft. The instrumentation box stays with the aircraft for its entire flight-test life.

The flight-test data processing requirements are split into real-time data collection for safe and efficient test conduct and postflight data processing. The USAF is responsible for the real-time collection, while the contractor team is responsible for the postflight processing. The contractor team and the USAF agreed to use the same computer software program to collect and process flight-test data in 1991.

Subsequent Flight-Test Activities: Raptors 01 and 02

With two test hops out of Dobbins ARB completed, Raptor 01 was transported via a Lockheed Martin C-5B Galaxy to the Air Force Flight Test Center at Edwards AFB, California, arriving there on February 5, 1998. The premier F-22 had been partially disassembled for its trip to Edwards. After its reassembly, it underwent a series of system functional checks.

Following its system functional tests, Raptor 01 performed a series of high-speed taxi tests, again to make sure that its nose wheel steering, brakes, flying surfaces, and so on worked properly. They did and the aircraft was cleared for flight. On May 17, 1998, nearly a year after its public debut in Marietta, Georgia, Raptor 01 made a successful third flight—its first at Edwards AFB.

After the flight, USAF Lt. Col. Steve Rainey said, "The aircraft handled like a dream," adding "It's the best flying aircraft I have flown, and it sets a new standard of excellence in fighter aviation." It was a true test flight with three objectives: envelope expansion flying qualities, speedbrake handling qualities, and formation flying qualities. Rainey said each of the three test points was flown precisely as briefed and that the flight was a successful test mission.

The aircraft had remained aloft 1 hour and 20 minutes. It was accompanied during all phases of flight by an F-15 flown by the first person to fly the aircraft, Lockheed Martin test pilot Metz; Raptor 01 checked out "Code One," meaning that the aircraft returned to base with no deficiencies and was ready to fly again.

Lt. Col. Rainey joined the F-22 System Program Office in 1994, and in 1996, became operations officer for the F-22 CTF at Edwards AFB. He was the first USAF pilot to fly the F-22A Raptor. Raptor 02 joined Raptor 01 at Edwards AFB on August 26, 1998. After its 10:35 A.M. EST (Eastern Standard Time) takeoff at Dobbins ARB, piloted by Lt. Col. Rainey, Raptor 02 flew nonstop cross country and landed at noon PST (Pacific Standard Time) on the main runway at Edwards. En route, the aircraft conducted several air refueling evaluations behind Boeing KC-135 Stratotankers. "The flight went exactly as planned," said Rainey, after the aircraft's first cross-continental flight. "I'm running out of adjectives to describe the way the F-22 flies. This is the best aircraft I've ever flown in aerial refueling. It is an extremely stable platform and a joy to fly." Rainey flew at 28,000 ft at Mn 0.7 during the 4½-hour flight. "We have achieved yet another milestone in the F-22 program," said Lt. Col. C. D. Moore, commander at the F-22 CTF at Edwards.

As had been reported earlier in September 1997, nine EMD F-22A Raptor aircraft (LMAS S/Ns 4001 to 4009) were to be used in the flight-test program. And during the EMD phase—scheduled to last until the year 2002—these nine aircraft are to fly approximately 2409 flights and cover some 4337 test hours, about 1.8 hours per flight per plane.

At the end of EMD in the year 2002, F-22A number 1 will be placed into flyable storage at Edwards AFB. The planned disposition of F-22A number 2 has not yet been determined. While F-22A number three is to be used for testing any nonavionics modifications or changes to the airframe (possibly a two-seat cockpit arrangement). At least three additional F-22As (which ones remain to be seen) will keep on flying for follow-on avionics testing (primarily the Block 4 avionics software that will include helmet-mounted cueing), AIM-9X Sidewinder missile integration, and Joint Tactical Information Distribution System (JTIDS) send-capability evaluations.

The last two EMD F-22As (4008 and 4009), featuring all the required improvements and changes needed for the first seven EMD Raptors, are essentially production-quality aircraft. Those two aircraft, in addition to the two production representative test vehicle (PRTV) aircraft (4010 and 4011), will be the four aircraft that the USAF will use for initial operational test and evaluation (IOT&E).

During IOT&E, the Air Force Operational Test and Evaluation Center at Kirtland AFB, New Mexico will operate the aircraft as an operational unit would. USAF crew chiefs and flight line maintenance personnel will maintain the aircraft. Dedicated IOT&E will run from mid-2002 until early 2003, and at the end of IOT&E, the AFOTEC will file its report to Congress attesting to the worthiness of the F-22A Raptor to enter into its full production status.

The nine EMD F-22A aircraft will be used primarily as follows:

4001   Flying qualities, flutter, loads, and high angle of attack; Avionics Block 1 configuration

4002   Propulsion, performance, and stores (internal/external) separation

4003   Flying qualities, flutter, loads, and GBU-32 JDAM integration; Avionics Block 2 configuration

4004   Integrated avionics, CNI (communication-navigation-identification), and low observables (stealth) testing

4005   Integrated avionics, radar, CNI, and armament

4006   Integrated avionics and observables testing; Avionics Block 3 configuration

4007   Integrated avionics and air vehicle performance (maximum rate of climb, speed, supercruise performance, etc.)

4008   USAF IOT&E, integrated avionics, and observables

4009   USAF IOT&E, integrated avionics, and low-observable tests

The first two EMD F-22A aircraft made their first flights in the late summer of 1997 (4001) and summer of 1998 (4002); the third was scheduled for summer of 1999 (4003). The last six of these EMD F-22A aircraft are scheduled (at this writing) to make their first flights in the fall of 1999 (4004), late spring of 2000 (4006), late summer of 2000 (4006), winter of 2000 (4007), spring of 2001 (4008), and winter of 2001 (4009), respectively.

Chuck Killberg, chief F-22 test pilot for Boeing, made his first flight on July 9, 1998 at Edwards AFB. It was the 12th flight of Raptor 01, which lasted 1.3 hours. During the flight, Killberg took the aircraft to 20,000 ft at a maximum speed of 250 knots (280 mph). The sortie tested a number of the Raptor's handling qualities and completed a number of propulsion system test points, including several in-flight engine restarts. He reported zero in-flight glitches. "We had a fantastic flight," Killberg said. "It was very much what we expected based on the simulations we've been doing for the past seven years. Of course, it was a fantastic opportunity for me, and I was thrilled to finally get into the air in the F-22."

Killberg joined Boeing as its F-22 chief test pilot in 1991. He has flown for more than 6000 hours in 140 types of aircraft, and manages Boeing's fleet of laboratory assets, including the 757 FTB. He made his second F-22 flight the following day, on July 10. The flight was a little shorter, at 1.1 hours. Killberg tested some of the aircraft's low-altitude handling qualities and conducted additional in-flight engine restarts.

Killberg is slated, at this writing, to make the first flight of Raptor 03 in the summer of 1999. The first flight of Raptor 03 will not be much different from those of Raptors 01 and 02. The aircraft is to fly a profile similar to that flown by Raptors 01 and 02 on their first flights, but the landing gear will be raised immediately after takeoff.

Raptor 03 is unique in other ways, however. It is the first EMD F-22A to have an internal structure that is fully representative of the production aircraft, and it is being used to perform demonstrations to 100 percent of the Raptor's structural loads. It is also the first Raptor used to test the operation of the advanced M-61A2 Vulcan cannon. It will also be used in acoustic surveys at Edwards AFB. In these surveys, the engines will be operated at various power settings from idle through maximum power to obtain data on the resulting structural effects and potential physiological effects on maintenance personnel.

Grounded Raptors

The fourth and fifth F-22s to roll out of the factory will never fly. These two F-22As are to remain on the ground at LMAS's Marietta facility for static loads testing and fatigue testing. These nonflying Raptors carry LMAS serial numbers 3999 and 4000, while the flying F-22As, as mentioned previously, list as 4001 through 4009.

Static loads testing on aircraft 3999 begins after the airplane is placed into a static testing fixture. The fixture allows loads to be applied to various parts of the airplane at varying degrees to test its structural strength under highly controlled and closely monitored conditions. Generally, these loads are applied to simulate loads experienced in actual flight.

In steps, the static test article is taken to the aircraft's load limit first; that is, the design limit of the structure. In the "ultimate test" the structure will be taken to 150 percent of its load limit. Successful completion clears EMD Raptor 03 to demonstrate maximum loads in flight.

All of these test results are used to update structural models, also called *finite element models* (FEMs). These models are representations of the airplane that break down its structure into discrete mathematical units called *elements*. The model is used as a basis for all structural analysis.

For fatigue testing, aircraft 4000 is placed in a test fixture similar to the one used for static loads test. The airframe is then loaded in many cycles over long periods to simulate stresses associated with expected operational use. The testing evaluates the durability of the airframe by "flying" it on the ground in a flight-by-flight manner around the clock. The airframe accumulates a lifetime of stresses in about 8 months of testing. The airframe will be put through two lifetimes to evaluate its basic durability. It will then be subjected to two more lifetimes of extended fatigue and damage tolerance testing.

Structures and Systems

One only has to look at a cutaway or phantom view illustration of the F-22A Raptor to see just how elaborate a modern weapon system actually is. However, both its manufacturers and its customers have worked together from the start to accomplish limited complexity throughout its incubation processes. In a multimission fighter, many interdependent structures and systems are required.

The Fuselage

Three major sections make up the F-22's fuselage structure. Front to back, these are the forward fuselage section, middle fuselage section, and aft fuselage section.

LMTAS built the Iron Bird to fully evaluate each of the F-22's ailerons, flaps, rudders, and other actuation devices; electrical wiring bundles and connections; hydraulic, oil, and other fluids' plumbing; and so on. In the first view the F-22 Iron Bird does not have the nose attached, while in the next view, the nose is attached. *(Lockheed Martin Corporation.)*

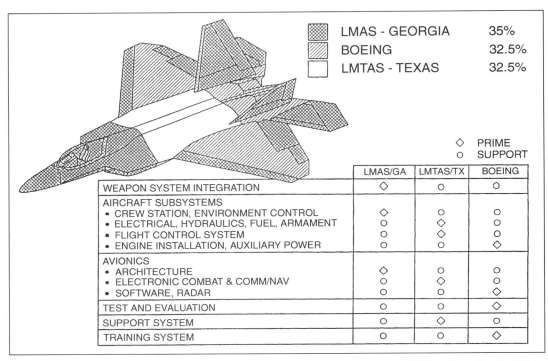

	LMAS/GA	LMTAS/TX	BOEING
WEAPON SYSTEM INTEGRATION	◇	○	○
AIRCRAFT SUBSYSTEMS			
• CREW STATION, ENVIRONMENT CONTROL	◇	○	○
• ELECTRICAL, HYDRAULICS, FUEL, ARMAMENT	○	◇	○
• FLIGHT CONTROL SYSTEM	○	◇	○
• ENGINE INSTALLATION, AUXILIARY POWER	○	○	◇
AVIONICS			
• ARCHITECTURE	◇	○	○
• ELECTRONIC COMBAT & COMM/NAV	○	◇	○
• SOFTWARE, RADAR	○	○	◇
TEST AND EVALUATION	○	○	◇
SUPPORT SYSTEM	○	◇	○
TRAINING SYSTEM	○	○	◇

◇ PRIME
○ SUPPORT

LMAS - GEORGIA   35%
BOEING   32.5%
LMTAS - TEXAS   32.5%

Money-based breakdown of F-22 prime and support work share between LMAS in Georgia, LMTAS in Texas, and Boeing in Seattle. *(Lockheed Martin Corporation.)*

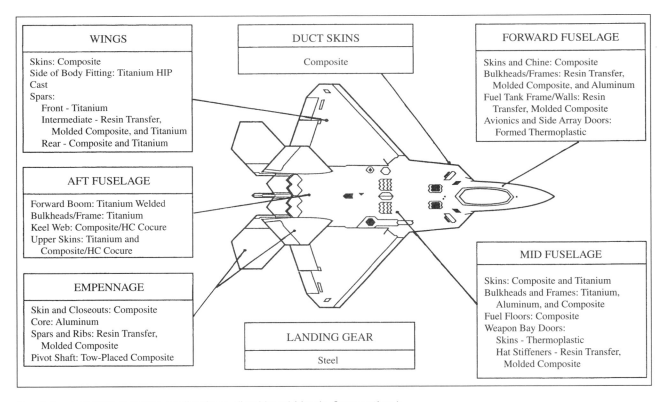

WINGS

Skins: Composite
Side of Body Fitting: Titanium HIP Cast
Spars:
    Front - Titanium
    Intermediate - Resin Transfer, Molded Composite, and Titanium
    Rear - Composite and Titanium

DUCT SKINS

Composite

FORWARD FUSELAGE

Skins and Chine: Composite
Bulkheads/Frames: Resin Transfer, Molded Composite, and Aluminum
Fuel Tank Frame/Walls: Resin Transfer, Molded Composite
Avionics and Side Array Doors: Formed Thermoplastic

AFT FUSELAGE

Forward Boom: Titanium Welded
Bulkheads/Frame: Titanium
Keel Web: Composite/HC Cocure
Upper Skins: Titanium and Composite/HC Cocure

EMPENNAGE

Skin and Closeouts: Composite
Core: Aluminum
Spars and Ribs: Resin Transfer, Molded Composite
Pivot Shaft: Tow-Placed Composite

LANDING GEAR

Steel

MID FUSELAGE

Skins: Composite and Titanium
Bulkheads and Frames: Titanium, Aluminum, and Composite
Fuel Floors: Composite
Weapon Bay Doors:
    Skins - Thermoplastic
    Hat Stiffeners - Resin Transfer, Molded Composite

Breakdown of F-22 material applications. *(Lockheed Martin Corporation.)*

Forward Fuselage Section

The forward fuselage section of the F-22 is manufactured by Lockheed Martin Aeronautical Systems (LMAS) in Marietta, Georgia. It consists of the structure aft of the radar bulkhead, the cockpit area, nose landing gear wheelwell, and F-1 fuel tank (the leading fuselage fuel tank). It is made up of approximately 3000 parts consisting mostly of aluminum alloys and composite materials. The forward fuselage also contains wiring harnesses, various types of tubing, cockpit instrument fixtures, avionics racks, and cockpit canopy mounts.

The F-22's forward fuselage section is slightly more than 17 ft long; measures a bit more than 5 ft wide at the widest point; 5 ft, 8 in high at the tallest point; and weighs about 1700 lb.

Made up in two sections, the forward fuselage is joined together by two long, and relatively wide side beams, and two longerons running the entire length of the assembly. The beams, manufactured of composite

The full-size F-22A Raptor Communication, Navigation, and Identification (CNI) model is located at Lockheed Martin Tactical Aircraft Systems' Fort Worth, Texas, CNI test area facilities. *(Lockheed Martin Corporation.)*

material, also provide an attachment point for the Raptor's *chine,* the outer fuselage edge that provides smooth aerodynamic blending into the engine air inlets and wings. The 17-ft-long aluminum alloy longerons form the sills of the F-22's cockpit, and the canopy rests on them.

This wind tunnel model (designated D-6) was used primarily to build the aerodynamic database for the F-22's design and is one of 23 models that were used in the Raptor's wind tunnel test program. A total of 16,930 wind tunnel test hours were completed validating the aerodynamic configuration of the F-22. *(Lockheed Martin Corporation.)*

Full-dome simulators for the F-22 at Fort Worth. *(Lockheed Martin Corporation.)*

With four 600-gal (2270-liter) external fuel tank facsimiles attached to the F-22 fuel system simulator, one of many fuel system tests is run at LMTAS. This is a test of the Raptor's center-of-gravity control. *(Lockheed Martin Corporation.)*

Beginning construction on Raptor 01 on November 2, 1995, LMAS employees Tommy Cole (left foreground) and L. D. Fleeman (left background) load the lower cap on to the nose landing gear wheelwell sidewall (known as a "web") while Dennis Watts (right foreground) checks one of the frames that will be attached to the web. Harold Morris (right background) is doing a preinstallation check on the other web. This was the first phase of building the first forward fuselage section. *(Lockheed Martin Corporation.)*

The cockpit canopy is also built by LMAS in Marietta, and is about 140 in long, 45 in wide, 27 in high, and weighs approximately 350 lb. To evaluate emergency cockpit canopy separation maneuvers, seven test canopies were built for the rocket-powered sled test program, which simulated emergency pilot-ejection activities.

The integrated forebody, also known as the *radar dome* (cover) or *radome*, is of composite material. It is manufactured by Lockheed Martin Skunk Works in Palmdale, California.

Middle Fuselage Section

The middle fuselage section is the largest and most complex of the F-22 assemblies. It is about 17 ft long, 15 ft wide, and 6 ft high; it weighs about 8500 lb.

The middle fuselage is considered to be the heart of the Raptor as almost every one of its systems pass through it, including the hydraulic, electrical, environmental control, and auxiliary power systems, as well as the aircraft's fuel. In addition, there are two fuel tanks (F-2 and F-3), four internal weapons bays (the two side bays, and the two sections of the main bay that is separated), the 20-mm cannon, and the auxiliary power unit (APU).

Middle fuselage bodies of the nine F-22 EMD aircraft are assembled at Lockheed Martin Tactical Aircraft Systems (LMTAS) in Fort Worth, Texas.

Aft Fuselage Section

The aft fuselage section is built by the Aircraft and Missile Systems Division of the Boeing Company in Seattle, Washington.

This is the second forward fuselage assembly to be built as it was loaded into its assembly fixture in January 1996. This part, called the *forward fuselage keel beam*, runs from nose wheelwell to the radar bulkhead along the bottom of the forward fuselage section. *(Lockheed Martin Corporation.)*

The aft fuselage section of the F-22 houses the two Pratt & Whitney F119 engines that power it. It also contains a major part of the aircraft's environmental control system and fuel, electrical, hydraulic, and engine subsystems. The aft fuselage section has to contend with the high heat from the engines as well as the stresses of supersonic speed and high-g maneuvers. The aft fuselage is 19 ft long and 12 ft wide, and weighs 5000 lb as shipped. It is 67 percent titanium alloys, 22 percent aluminum alloys and 11 percent composite materials by weight.

About 25 percent (by weight) of the aft fuselage consists of large electron-beam-welded titanium alloy forward and aftward booms. The largest of these booms, the forward boom, is more than 10 ft long and weighs about 650 lb. The welded booms of the aft fuselage are extremely weight-efficient and greatly reduce the use of traditional fasteners (rivets, etc.) by about 75 percent. A major part of the F-22's aftward fuselage section is the empennage or tail group. The empennage consists of the vertical and horizontal tailplanes. The two vertical stabilizers (each one having a rudder) are of a multiple spar construction, and feature hot isostatic pressed (HIP) cast rudder actuator housings. The edges and rudders are made of composite materials, and both surfaces (the unmoving vertical tails and movable rudders) have embedded very high-frequency (VHF) antennas, as well as other antennas. The rudders can be deflected outward to act as speed brakes.

The horizontal tailplanes, known as *stabilators* (combined horizontal stabilizers and elevators), are made of honeycomb materials with composite edges. They are all-moving assemblies and are deflected up and down by the composite pivot shaft (CPS). The F-22's stabilators are all movable and close-coupled. They are mounted directly aft the wings on the very same plane and their entire bodies deflect both up and down, and they are fitted so close that the leading edges of their apexes fit right into the inboard trailing edges of the wings.

The F-22 midfuselage section production area in one of LMTAS's Fort Worth plant buildings. *(Lockheed Martin Corporation.)*

An F-22 midfuselage section moves toward its final assembly area. *(Lockheed Martin Corporation.)*

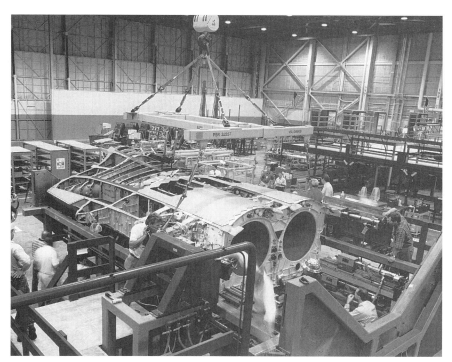

A close-up view of an F-22 midfuselage section as it is placed in to its final assembly area at Fort Worth. *(Lockheed Martin Corporation.)*

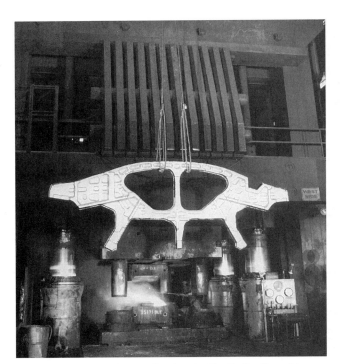

Manufactured by Wyman Gordon in North Grafton, Massachusetts, this midfuselage bulkhead is the world's largest titanium alloy forging. *(Lockheed Martin Corporation.)*

The Wings

Boeing manufactures the wings for the F-22, minus the leading-edge flaps, trailing edge flaps, ailerons, and their related parts. Each of the F-22's wings measures 16 ft (side of body) by 18 ft (leading edge) and is roughly triangular in shape. Together, the wings give the Raptor's planform a modified delta shape. The thin wings are designed to cruise at supersonic speeds for extended periods and to withstand extremely high-*g* maneuvers.

By weight, the Boeing-built portion of the wing is 42 percent titanium alloy; 35 percent composite materials; and 23 percent aluminum alloy, steel alloy, and other materials such as fasteners and clips. Each wing weighs about 2000 lb.

Traditional aircraft materials such as aluminum alloys and steel alloys make up only about 20 percent of the F-22's structure by weight. The high-performance capabilities of the Raptor requires a significant use of titanium alloys (42 percent of all structural material) and composite materials (24 percent). Both titanium alloys and composite materials are stronger and lighter than aluminum and steel, and offer better protection against corrosion. Titanium also offers higher temperature resistance—an especially useful characteristic near the exhaust nozzles of the F119 engines.

Another Wyman Gordon bulkhead is attached to the F-22's midfuselage section. *(Lockheed Martin Corporation.)*

Boeing crane operators and assembly mechanics load a "center keel" for the first Raptor's aft fuselage section into an assembly fixture. *(The Boeing Company.)*

On September 26, 1996, Boeing employees moved the titanium alloy and composite material aft fuselage section for the first of nine EMD F-22As into position for high-precision automated drilling. A data-driven, laser-guided drilling machine then drilled more than 2000 holes into the structure. *(The Boeing Company.)*

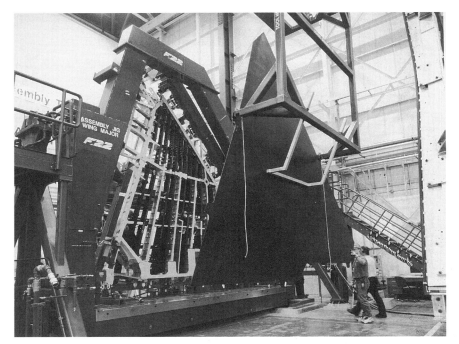

The wings of Raptor 01 are shown in final assembly on May 29, 1996 at a Boeing facility in Seattle. Each F-22 wing measures about 16 ft (side of body) by 18 ft (leading edge) and weighs about 2000 lb on completion. *(The Boeing Company.)*

The first Raptor takes shape; the Boeing-built wings of the first EMD F-22 are being mated (final processes) to the aircraft's fuselage. The aircraft's forward fuselage section was built by LMAS, the midfuselage section by LMTAS, and the aft fuselage section by Boeing. *(Lockheed Martin Corporation.)*

Airframe Structural Materials by Weight

The current F-22 weight distribution is as follows: titanium alloy 64 (Ti-64), 36 percent; thermoset composites, 24 percent; aluminum alloy (Al), 16 percent; other materials, 15 percent; steel alloy, 6 percent; titanium alloy 62222 (Ti-62222), 3 percent; and thermoplastic composites, 1 percent. (Other materials include coatings, paint, transparency, radome, tires, brakes, sealants, adhesives, seals, actuators, gases, and fluids.) Different titanium alloys have different applications on the F-22. Ti-62222 is a very high-strength alloy that was introduced on the Raptor.

On the F-22, the number of parts made from thermoset composites is about a 50/50 split between epoxy resin parts and bismaleimide (BMI) parts. The aircraft's exterior skins are all BMI, which offer high strength and high temperature resistance. Thermoplastic composites are also highly durable materials but, unlike thermosets, thermoplastics can be reheated and re-formed.

The AirMet 100 steel alloy used in the F-22's main landing gear is another innovation. It is one of the first applications of a special heat treatment of steel, which provides greater corrosion protection to the main landing gear piston axle.

The Pratt & Whitney F119-PW-100 Turbofan Engine

The Pratt & Whitney F119-PW-100 turbofan engine is a radical advance in fighter aircraft propulsion. The F119 engine develops more than twice the thrust of current engines under supersonic conditions, and more thrust *without* afterburner than conventional engines *with* afterburner.

The F-22 is powered by two of these revolutionary 35,000-lb thrust class (the actual maximum thrust rating is classified) F119 turbofan engines. By comparison, the engines powering the USAF's current F-15 and F-16 fighters have maximum thrust ratings ranging from 23,000 to 29,000 lb.

Fighter aircraft propulsive systems achieve additional thrust by directly injecting fuel into the exhaust fire of a jet engine. This process, called *afterburning,* gives a fighter aircraft a rocketlike boost of speed as the fuel ignites within a jet engine's exhaust chamber. The penalties are increased fuel consumption, greater heat, and worse, a greater infrared or heat signature visibility to the enemy.

The design requirement called for the two F119s in the Raptor to propel it to speeds above Mn 1.5 (the actual Mach number is classified) without the use of afterburners. This gives the Raptor a greater operating range and stealthier flight operation.

F119-PW-100 Features

The F119 required a great deal of risky innovation to achieve its goals. These included the following:

- *Integrally bladed rotors.* In most stages, disks and blades are machined from a single piece of metal alloy for better performance and less air leakage.

- *Long chord, shroudless fan blades.* Wider, stronger fan blades eliminate the need for the shroud, a ring of metal around most jet engine fans. Both the wider blades and the shroudless design enhance engine efficiency.

- *Low-aspect, high-stage-load compressor blades.* Once again, wider blades offer greater strength and efficiency.

- *Alloy C high-strength burn-resistant titanium compressor stators.* P&W's innovative titanium alloy increases stator durability, allowing the engine to run hotter and faster for greater thrust and efficiency.

- *Alloy C in augmentor (afterburner) and exhaust nozzle.* The same heat-resistant titanium alloy protects aft components, permitting greater thrust and durability.

- *Floatwall combustor.* Thermally isolated panels of oxidation-resistant high-cobalt material make the combustion chamber more durable, which helps reduce powerplant maintenance.

- *No visible smoke.* This reduces the possibility of an enemy visually detecting the engine exhaust of an F-22.

- *Improved supportability.* All components, harnesses, and plumbing are located on the bottom of the F119 engine for easy access. All line replaceable units (LRUs) are located one deep (units are not located on top of one another). In addition, each LRU can be removed with just one of the six standard tools required for engine maintenance.

- *Fourth-generation full-authority digital electronic engine control* (FADEC). Dual-redundant digital engine controls—two units per engine, two computers per unit—ensure unmatched reliability in F-22 engine control systems. The same experience that introduced full-authority digital control to fighter engines works with the aircraft system to make the powerplant and the airframe function together as a single flight unit.

Pratt & Whitney's balanced approach to the F119 design process, using a team approach called *integrated product development* (IPD), led to an engine as innovative in its reliability and support as in its overall performance. Assemblers and flight line mechanics participated in the F119's design from its inception. The result is that ease of assembly, maintenance, and repair are designed into the engine.

The F119 has 40 percent fewer major parts than do current fighter aircraft engines, and each existing part is more durable and does its job more efficiently. Computational fluid dynamics (CFD)—the study of airflow using advanced computers—led to the design of

A Pratt & Whitney F119-PW-100 engine is shown hanging from one of P&W's old J75 turbojet engine (the engine used by the USAF F-105 Thunderchief and F-106 Delta Dart fighters) slings. Two F119s, without their afterburners in operation, propel the F-22 past Mn 1.5. *(Pratt & Whitney Large Military Engines.)*

The Lockheed Martin F-117A *Nighthawk,* which was a third-generation stealth aircraft, was a Skunk Works achievement just like its SR-71A *Blackbird* stable mate—the first-generation stealth aircraft. The *Have Blue* prototypes were the second-generation. The fourth-generation is the Northrop Grumman B-2A *Spirit,* while the fifth-generation is the Lockheed Martin/Boeing F-22A *Raptor.* Thus, Lockheed is the hands-down leader in the creation of stealth aircraft products. Here are 17 F-117s at Langley AFB in late 1990, just before they were flown to Saudi Arabia for subsequent action in Desert Storm. *(U.S. Air Force.)*

During its official unveiling ceremony inside Lockheed Martin's Plant 10 facility in Palmdale, California, the first of two Lockheed/Boeing/General Dynamics (now Lockheed Martin/Boeing) YF-22A prototypes appears publicly for the first time on August 28, 1990. *(Lockheed Martin Corporation.)*

Flying from Palmdale to Edwards AFB on September 29, 1990, the General Electric YF120-powered YF-22A made its first flight with Lockheed ATF chief test pilot David L. ("Dave") Ferguson at its controls. As a matter of historical significance, Dave Ferguson was the second person to fly the Lockheed Martin F-117A Nighthawk, the world's first, and still only, Stealth light-attack bombardment aircraft. *(Lockheed Martin Corporation.)*

The Pratt & Whitney YF119-powered YF-22A made its first flight on October 30, 1990 with Lockheed test pilot Tom Morgenfeld in its seat. *(Lockheed Martin Corporation.)*

With their first flights respectively occurring on August 27 and October 26, 1990 at Edwards AFB, the two Northrop/McDonnell Douglas YF-23A ATF prototypes fly in formation, circa late 1990. First to fly, the black one (YF119-powered) was nicknamed the *Black Widow II*. Second to fly, the multihued light to medium gray one (YF-120-powered) was dubbed the *Gray Ghost. (U.S. Air Force.)*

Powered by two Pratt & Whitney YF119-PW-100 prototype engines, the YF-22A prototype 2 (87-0701) flies near Edwards AFB. This is the airframe-powerplant combination that the USAF selected for what has now become the F-22A Raptor. The YF-22A's nose landing gear retracted aft while the F-22A's retracts forward. *(Lockheed Martin Skunk Works.)*

This is another view of the YF119-powered YF-22A, with its landing gear now retracted, near Edwards AFB, in late 1991. With Tom Morgenfeld at its controls, it resumed flight test activities on November 30, 1991 with a 1.6-hour flight. Originally owned by Lockheed and marked with civilian registration number N22YX, it was remarked with USAF serial no. 87-0701 after it was purchased by the USAF. *(Lockheed Martin Skunk Works.)*

F119-PW-100

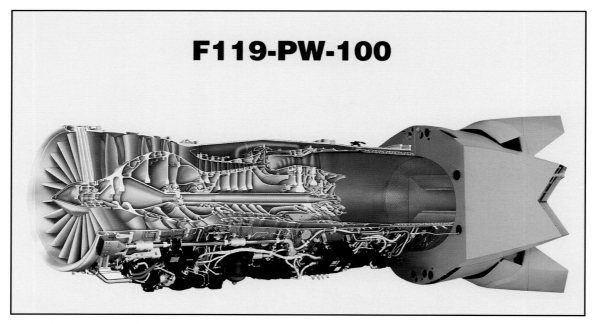

Although the Pratt & Whitney F119-PW-100 engine does not appear very complicated in this phantom view, it is an extremely advanced propulsion unit. It develops more than twice the thrust of current engines under supersonic conditions, and more thrust without afterburner than conventional engines with afterburner. *(Pratt & Whitney Large Military Engines.)*

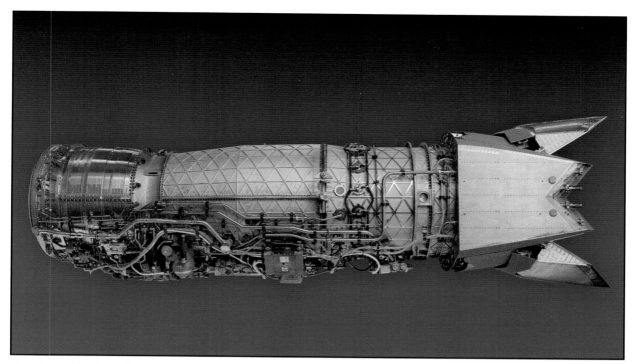

Two Pratt & Whitney F119-PW-100 turbofan engines with a combined thrust output of 70,000 lb propel the F-22A Raptor. Since the maximum gross takeoff weight of a full-production Raptor is to be about 60,000 lb, the aircraft will have a tremendous engine power (thrust) : airframe weight (pounds) ratio permitting the F-22A to rapidly accelerate while flying straight up. *(Pratt & Whitney Large Military Engines.)*

With Lockheed Martin F-22 Raptor chief test pilot A. Paul Metz standing nearby, the large-scale F-22 paint application test model is shown. By using a highly sophisticated and fully computerized robot paint machine, Lockheed Martin can automatically paint the nine EMD F-22As as well as the 330 subsequent-production Raptors with predetermined paint schemes. *(Lockheed Martin Corporation.)*

With "Spirit of America" emblazoned on its left side, the first of nine EMD F-22A Raptors, called *Raptor 01,* is spotlighted during its heavily attended public debut on April 9, 1997. The "Spirit of America" banner was later removed and was not present when the aircraft made its first flight about 5 months later. *(Lockheed Martin Corporation.)*

With Paul Metz at the controls, on September 7, 1997, Raptor 01 graces the skies near Marietta, Georgia. Similar in size and weight to its immediate predecessor, the Eagle, operational Raptors will take over the F-15C's air superiority role. *(The Boeing Company.)*

Raptor 02 departs Dobbins ARB on June 29, 1998 for its first flight. The shape of the F-22 perhaps contributes to the most important part of its stealth capability. *(Lockheed Martin Corporation.)*

As it banks to the right, Raptor 02 (AF 91-0002) flies through cumulus and cirrus clouds. Using its afterburners, the F-22 is capable of more than Mach number 2 (Mn 2+) at altitude (Mn 1.5+ without afterburners) and Mn 1+ at sea level. *(Lockheed Martin Corporation.)*

The F-22 features two wide-chord, large-area vertical tails with large-area rudders. Canted outward for stealth reasons, its vertical tails offer excellent low-, medium- and high-speed stability. The ED on the tail denotes Edwards AFB. *(Lockheed Martin Corporation.)*

During its third flight test out of Edwards AFB, the second of nine EMD F-22A Raptors—the Raptor 02—flies over Rogers Dry Lake near the USAF's Air Force Flight Test Center and NASA's Dryden Flight Research Center. *(Lockheed Martin Corporation.)*

An F119 engine being test-run in afterburner. Although the F-119's thrust vectoring exhaust nozzles are relatively heavy, they enhance the F-22's performance. *(Pratt & Whitney Large Military Engines.)*

engine turbomachinery of unprecedented efficiency, giving the F119 more thrust with fewer turbine stages.

F119/F-22 Engine Exhaust Nozzle

The F119 engine exhaust nozzle for the Raptor is the world's first full-production vectoring nozzle, fully integrated into the airframe-powerplant combination as original equipment.

The two-dimensional nozzle vectors engine thrust 20° up and 20° down for improved aircraft agility. This vectoring increases the roll rate of the F-22 by 50 percent and has features that contribute to the aircraft's stealth requirements. Heat-resistant components give the nozzles the durability needed to vector engine thrust, even while the afterburners are in use. With precision digital controls, the nozzles work like another flight control surface on the Raptor. Thrust vectoring is an integrated part of the F-22's flight control system, which allows for seamless integration of all components working in response to pilot commands.

The nozzle assemblies are manufactured at Pratt & Whitney's West Palm Beach, Florida, facility. This is Pratt & Whitney's Large Military Engine design and prototype construction facility.

F119 Production Schedule

In the Engineering and Manufacturing Development (EMD) phase of the F-22 Raptor program, Pratt & Whitney is continuing the design, development, and qualification processes of three products: 26 EMD flight test F119 engines, the F119 engine support system, and the F119 engine training system.

At this writing, for the current production total of 339 F-22 Raptor aircraft, Pratt & Whitney will manufacture 775 F119 engines. This number will provide engines for the 339

General Electric's YF120-GE-100 engine. Although it pushed a YF-23A ATF prototype to a still-classified top speed, it lost out to P&W's YF119-PW-100 engine. Compare this photo with that of the F119 engine on page 50 to see the difference in their exterior plumbing and thrust vectoring exhaust nozzles. *(General Electric.)*

planned aircraft (two per aircraft) plus sufficient spares; 22 of these 775 engines are for the nine EMD F-22 aircraft (two per aircraft) plus spares.

F-22 Airframe-Mounted Accessory Drive

Built by Boeing, the F-22 Airframe Mounted Accessory Drive (AMAD) transfers shaft power from the Air Turbine Starter System (ATSS) to the F119 engines for engine starts, and from the engines to a generator and hydraulic pumps for the electrical and hydraulic systems.

The AMAD transmits power required by the high-performance F-22 throughout the flight envelope and incorporates a highly reliable lubrication system that services the AMAD-mounted generator and ATSS as well as gearbox components.

F119 Engine Trailer

The Boeing-developed F119 engine trailer (designated A/M32M-34) is an important piece of ground support equipment that is required for removal and installation of the F-22's engines. The trailer also supports the engine for on-base towing, air transport, and ground transport shipments. For both air and ground shipments a shipping adapter (a support frame that fits over the top of the engine and attaches to the trailer to secure the engine) is also required.

During engine installation, the trailer provides a five-axis (vertical, lateral, pitch, roll, and yaw) adjustment capability to precisely align the engine to the aircraft. Fine adjustments in the vertical and lateral directions are also provided for load transfer of the engine to and from the aircraft.

Once aligned, the engine slides from the trailer's rails directly to a similar set of extension rails placed in the aircraft's engine bay. From there, the engine is pushed onto the engine mounts. The lower segments of two of the aircraft's engine bay frames (numbers 5 and 6) drop down to allow for engine fitting.

Only eight connections have to be made between the powerplant and the airframe, and with the dropout links, maintenance personnel will be able to remove and replace an engine in about 75 minutes. The A/M32M-34 engine trailer is about 14 ft long and 6 ft wide, and has an empty weight of 3400 lb; maximum payload capacity is 7500 lb. When fully lowered by means of its mechanically actuated scissors-lift assembly, the trailer's height is only 38 in; maximum height is 5 ft.

Flight-Critical Avionics and Systems

To successfully create and market such an advanced tactical fighter as the F-22, its designers and developers had to incorporate numerous flight-critical avionics and systems, which are described in the text below.

Vehicle Management System

The *vehicle management system* (VMS) provides flight and propulsion control. The VMS enables the pilot to maneuver the F-22 to its maximum capabilities. The system includes hardware, such as the control stick, throttle controls, rudder pedals and actuators, air data probes, accelerometers, leading-edge flap drive actuators, and the primary flight control actuators. The VMS also encompasses the software that controls these devices; the VMS became operational when Raptor 01 was flown for the first time in September 1997.

The flight control software and flight control laws that underpin the VMS are tested in a specialized laboratory at LMTAS in Fort Worth. The *VMS Integration Facility* (VIF), as this lab is called, consists of an F-22 cockpit and flightworthy F-22 hardware and software. The VIF has been operational since March 1995.

Utilities and Subsystems

The utilities and systems for the F-22 include these subsystems: the integrated vehicle subsystem controller, environmental control system, fire protection, auxiliary power-generating system, landing gear, fuel system, electrical system, hydraulics, and arresting system.

Integrated Vehicle Subsystem Controller (IVSC)

The IVSC is the system responsible for aircraft integration, control, and diagnostics.

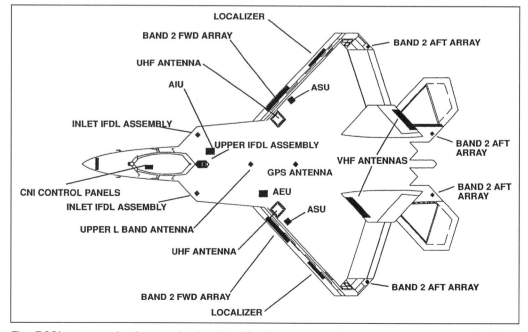

The F-22's communications-navigation-identification upper-surface aperture locations. *(Lockheed Martin Corporation.)*

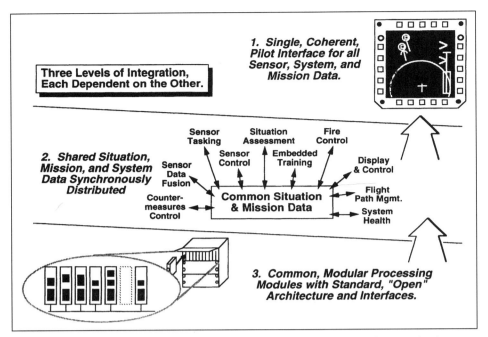

The F-22's three-level integrated avionics system. *(Lockheed Martin Corporation.)*

Environmental Control System (ECS)

The F-22 uses a totally integrated ECS that provides thermal conditioning throughout the flight envelope for the pilot and the avionics. The five basic safety-critical functions the ECS must take care are avionics cooling, adequate air to the pilot, cockpit canopy defogging, cockpit pressurization, and fire protection.

Air Cycle System (ACS)

The air cycle system takes bleed air from the F-22's two engines (which enters the system at 1200 to 2000°F and cools it down in the primary heat exchanger (PHX) to approximately 400°F. From the heat exchanger, the air is fed into the air cycle refrigeration package (ACRP). The air must be dry, so the system also includes water extractors.

When the air comes out of the ACRP, it is chilled to approximately 50°F. The flight-critical equipment is cooled by this air. This air is also fed into the Normalair-Garrett-built onboard oxygen-generating system to provide breathable oxygen to the pilot, to operate the breathing regulator/anti-*g* (antigravity) valve on the pilot's ensemble, to provide canopy defogging and cockpit pressurization.

Liquid Cooling System

Unlike other fighter aircraft, the F-22 uses liquid cooling, rather than air cooling, for the mission avionics. The Raptor is breaking new ground in liquid cooling and the environment in which it works. Resistance to high temperature and durability were the driving factors in the liquid cooling design. Allied Signal is the primary supplier of the liquid cooling equipment.

The closed-loop liquid cooling system is divided into two loops: one forward and one aft. These systems use brushless, direct-current (DC) motor pumps that are connected for redundancy. The medium used in the liquid cooling system is polyalphaolefin) (PAO).

The forward loop is used to cool the mission-critical avionics and keep them at a comfortable (for them) 68°F. The PAO passes through the vapor cycle system, and a filter, and is routed to the avionics and then out to the wings to cool the embedded, or blended, sensors.

From there, the now-warm PAO coolant enters the aft loop, which allows it to pass by the air cycle machine, which cools the system by receiving transferred heat. The PAO then is routed to the fuel tanks, where the heat is dumped. No coolant is mixed in the fuel, however, as this is a closed-looped cooling system. The fuel in the tanks is used only as a heat sink.

Thermal Management System (TMS)

The thermal management system is used to keep the aircraft's fuel cool. The *air-cooled fuel cooler* (ACFC) takes air from the boundary layer diverter between the engine air inlets and the aircraft's forward fuselage section. Hot fuel passes through the heat exchanger and cools it down. "Greatly simplified," as Lockheed Martin describes it, "this is essentially blowing on hot soup to cool it down enough to eat it."

Fire Protection

Fire protection is provided for the F-22's engine bays, the APU, and for dry bays such as the landing gear wells, the side-of-body cavities, the linear linkless ammunition handling system (LLAHS), the onboard inert-gas generation system, left and right air-cooled fuel coolers, and the environmental control system bay.

The Raptor uses infrared and ultraviolet sensors for fire detection and Halon 1301 for fire suppression. The Halon 1301 is the only ozone-depleting chemical on the F-22, and efforts are under way to find a replacement suppressing chemical.

Auxiliary Power Generation System (APGS)

The APGS for the F-22 is being developed, built, and tested by Allied Signal Aerospace for Boeing. The APGS consists of an auxiliary power unit (APU), and a self-contained stored energy system (SES). The APGS provides secondary aircraft power for everyday main engine ground start, aircraft ground maintenance, and in-flight emergency power for aircraft recovery. The APGS uses the G-250 APU, a 450-horsepower turbine engine that uses state-of-the-art materials and design resulting in the highest power density APU in the industry (horsepower:weight ratio).

Fuel System

There are eight fuel tanks on the F-22, including one (designated F-1) in the forward fuselage section behind the pilot's ejection seat. The other seven tanks are located in the middle and aft fuselage sections (three: F-2, F-3, and F-4) and the wings (four: W-1L and W-2L/W-3R and W-4R). The Raptor will burn Jet Petroleum formula eight or JP-8, a naphthalene-based fuel with a relatively high flash point. The F-22 has a single-point ground-fueling receptacle, and it can be refueled without the need for ground power. It also has a Xar-made aerial refueling receptacle on the topside of the aircraft in the center of the fuselage directly behind the cockpit. It is covered by two butterfly doors that have integral low-voltage lights to aid boom operators during night refueling operations.

The F-22 also has the OBIGGS equipment that renders the fuel tanks inert as the fuel is depleted. By filling the tanks with inert nitrogen gas as the fuel is used, the fumes are suppressed, and the chance of explosion from gunfire or other ignition source is nearly eliminated.

F-22 Avionics System

The requirements for the F-22's avionics system are derived from the F-22 weapon system concept, which presented the guiding principles for the overall weapons system. The integrated avionics system is one of the essential elements that will give the Raptor the tactical advantage it needs over the fighter threats of the future. The other essential elements

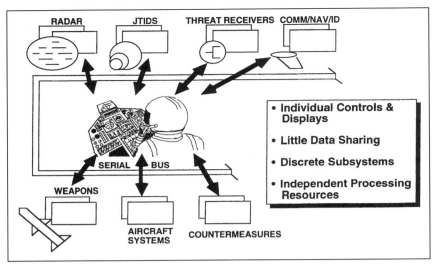

The federated avionics system for the current generation of EMD F-22 aircraft.
(Lockheed Martin Corporation.)

include stealth, maneuverability, and supercruise capability, aided by the aircraft's first-look, first-shoot, and first-kill capability.

Avionics System Design

Translating the system requirements into a producible, affordable, and maintainable design has been the work of the EMD program so far. The basic concept, derived from the Pave Pillar program in the 1980s [which included development of integrated communications, navigation, identification avionics (ICNIA) and integrated electronic warfare system (INEWS) systems], was to provide all the signal and data processing resources in a central collection of modular processors, linked to the sensors, subsystems, and pilot by way of high-speed data buses. The F-22 architecture provides just such a system, interfaced to the air-cooled, flight safety-critical systems such as the aircraft's flight control system.

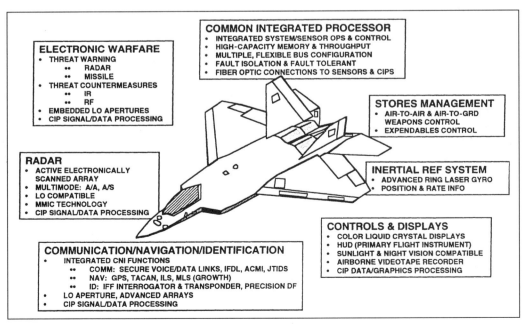

The F-22's integrated avionics subsystems are illustrated. *(Lockheed Martin Corporation.)*

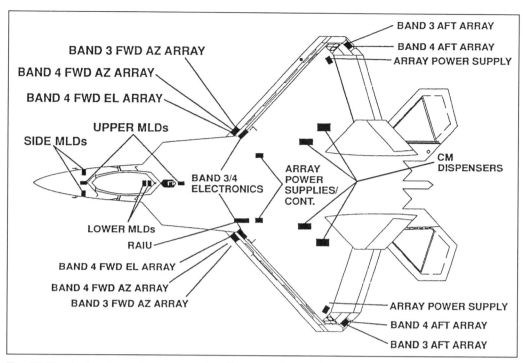

The F-22's electronic warfare or (EW) locations are shown. *(Lockheed Martin Corporation.)*

Common Integrated Processor

The Hughes-built Common Integrated Processor (CIP) is the brain of the F-22's avionics system. Rather than the radar system, the ICNIA system, and the INEWS system having individual processors, the CIP, which is not much bigger than a breadbox, supports all signal and data processing for all sensors and mission avionics.

Striking the now-classic Boeing pose near Washington's Mount Rainier as so many of its aircraft have, still without its sensor wing, the 757 FTB heads south on a flight out of Seattle. *(The Boeing Company.)*

There are two CIPs in each F-22A, with 66 module slots per CIP. They have identical backplanes, and all the Raptor's processing requirements can be handled by only seven different types of processors. Currently (early 1999), 19 of 66 slots in CIP number 1 and 22 of 66 slots in CIP number 2 are not populated and are available for growth. Each CIP module is limited by design to only 70 percent of its capability, so the F-22 has 30 percent growth capability with no change to the existing equipment. There are space, power, and cooling provisions in the aircraft for a third CIP, so the requirement for a 200 percent avionics growth capability in the F-22 can be met easily.

AN/APG-77 Radar

The Raptor's Northrop Grumman/Texas Instruments-built AN/APG-77 radar is an active-element, electronically scanned (nonmoving) array that features a separate transmitter and receiver for each of the antenna's several thousand, finger-sized radiating elements. Most of the mechanical parts common to other radars have been eliminated, thus making the radar more reliable.

This type of radar antenna, which is integrated both physically and electromagnetically with the airframe, provides the frequency agility, low radar cross section (RCS), and wide bandwidth necessary to support the F-22's air dominance mission.

The AN/APG-77 radar system is paramount to the F-22's integrated avionics and sensor capabilities. It will provide pilots with detailed information about multiple threats before the adversary's radar ever detects the Raptor.

Avionics Software

The software that provides the avionics system's full functionality is composed of approximately 1.7 million lines of code. In addition, 90 percent of the software is written in Ada, the DoD's common triservice high-order computer language. Exceptions to the Ada requirement are granted only for special processing or maintenance requirements. When the first Raptor made its first flight in September 1997, it carried only 20 percent of the final software load that will be required for the full avionics suite.

The avionics software is to be integrated in three blocks, each building on the capability of the previous block.

Block 1 is primarily radar capability, but Block 1 does contain more than 50 percent of the avionics suite's full-functionality source lines of code or SLOC and provides end-to-end capability for the sensor-to-pilot data flow. The fourth EMD F-22 will be the first raptor to have a full avionics suite, and at this writing, it was scheduled to fly in late 1999.

Block 2 is the start of sensor fusion. It adds radio-frequency coordination, reconfiguration, and some electronic warfare functions. Block 2 is to be integrated into the F-22 in late 1999.

Block 3 encompasses full sensor fusion built on electronic warfare and CNI functions. It has an embedded training capability and provides for electronic counter-countermeasures (ECCM). It is scheduled to be integrated into the aircraft in the spring of 2000. *Block 3.1,* which adds full GBU-32 JDAM launch capability and joint tactical information distribution system (JTIDS) receive-only capability, will be integrated in April 2000.

The proposed *Block 4* software will be post-EMD. It is scheduled to be integrated on the IOC F-22s in 2005 and will likely include helmet-mounted cueing, AIM-9X Sidewinder missile integration, and JTIDS send-only capability.

The Cockpit

The F-22 Raptor's cockpit represents a revolution over current "pilot offices," as it is optimized to allow the pilot to operate as a tactician, not a sensor operator. "For the human is

This is the first cockpit canopy for the first Raptor as it appeared in January 1996. It is approximately 140 in long and 45 in wide and weighs about 350 lb. *(Lockheed Martin Corporation.)*

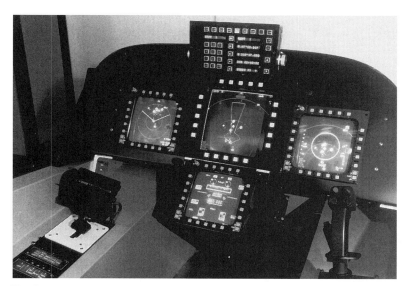

The Boeing-developed tactical displays for the F-22 are shown on this simulator. The defense display on the left gives pilots the information they need to protect themselves against threats. The situation display in the middle provides them with overall situation awareness and navigation information. The attack display on the right gives them the information necessary to attack a target. *(The Boeing Company.)*

a good differentiator, but a poor integrator," according to Lockheed Martin. It added, "the F-22 cockpit lets the pilot do what humans do best, and it fully utilizes the power of the computer to do what it does best."

While that change to tactician is the biggest advance the F-22's cockpit has over current fighter cockpits, there are several other distinctive features, including

- The F-22's cockpit is one of the very first "all-glass" cockpits for tactical fighter aircraft—there are no traditional round-dial standby or dedicated instrument gauges.

- It accommodates the largest range of pilots by size (the central 99 percent of the USAF pilot population) of any tactical fighter aircraft.

- It is the first baseline night-vision goggle or (NVG)-compatible cockpit.

- It has designed-in growth capability for helmet-mounted systems.

- The canopy is the largest piece of polycarbonate formed in the world with the greatest zone 1 (highest-quality) optics for compatibility with helmet-mounted systems.

The Raptor's cockpit design also ensures pilot safety with an improved version of the proven zero/zero (zero altitude/zero speed) Boeing Advanced Concept Ejection Seat (ACES II) ejection seat and a new pilot personal equipment and life support ensemble.

Pilot/Air Vehicle Interface

The Head-Up Display (HUD), supplied by GEC-Marconi Avionics, offers a wide field of view (30° horizontally and 25° vertically) and serves as a primary flight instrument for the pilot. The F-22's HUD mounts atop and directly in the center of the main control panel immediately in front of the pilot's eyes. It is approximately 4.5 in high and uses standardized symbology developed by the Air Force Instrument Flight Center (AFIFC). It does not present information in color, but the tactical symbol set is the same that is used on the Raptor's Head-Down Display (HDD) screens.

During F-22 canopy bird strike tests, it was found that the HUD combiner glass would shatter the canopy. To solve this problem for all nine of the F-22 EMD aircraft, the Raptor's HUD now has a rubber buffer strip on it that will effectively shield the polycarbonate of the canopy from a bird strike. Design is also underway for a HUD that will collapse during a bird strike, but would remain upright under all conditions. Additionally, investigations are ongoing into the possibility of having the HUD combiner glass laminated similar to household safety glass to prevent flying glass in the cockpit following a bird strike.

The integrated control panel (ICP) is the primary means for manual pilot data entry for communications, navigation, and automatic pilot information. Located under the glare shield and HUD, this keypad entry system also has some double-click functions, much like a computer mouse for rapid pilot access and/or use.

Another view of an F-22 cockpit simulator shows a pilot firing a missile launch at a target. Note right hand on control stick and thumb on fire button. *(Lockheed Martin Corporation.)*

There are six liquid crystal display (LCD) panels in the cockpit. These present information in full color and are fully readable in direct sunlight. The LCD panels offer lower weight and less area than the cathode-ray tube (CRT) displays used in most current aircraft. The lower power requirements of LCD panels also provide a reliability improvement over CRTs.

The two up-front display (UFD) panels measure 3 in by 4 in in size and are located to the left and right of the ICP discussed above. The UFD panels are used to display integrated caution-advisory-warning data and communications-navigation-identification data and serve as the *standby flight instrumentation group* and *fuel quantity indicator* suite.

The standby flight group (SFG) is always in operation and, although it is presented on LCD panel displays, it shows the basic information (attitude indicator, rate of climb/descent, etc.) the pilot needs to fly the aircraft. The SFG is tied to the last source of power in the aircraft, so if everything else fails, the pilot will still be able to fly the aircraft.

The primary multiple-function display (PMFD) is an 8-by-8-in color display that is located in the middle of the main instrument panel, under the ICP discussed above. It is the pilot's principal display for aircraft navigation (including showing waypoints and route of flight) and situation assessment or a "God's-eye view" of the entire environment around (above, below, both sides, front and back) the aircraft.

Three secondary multiple function display (SMFD) screens are all 6.25 in by 6.25 in, and two of them are located on either side of the PMFD on the instrument panel with the third underneath the PMFD between the pilot's knees. These are used for displaying tactical information (both defensive and offensive) as well as nontactical data such as checklists, subsystem status, engine thrust output, and stores management.

Cockpit Display Symbology

The tactical information shown on the displays is designed to be intuitively recognized by pilots so that they can be aware of the situation around them by a glance at the screen. Enemy aircraft are shown as red triangles, friendly aircraft are green circles, unknown aircraft are shown as yellow squares, and wingmen are shown as blue F-22s. Surface-to-air missile sites are represented by pentagons (along with an identification of exactly the type of missile and its lethal range).

There are further refinements to the shape and color of the *symbols*. A filled-in triangle means that the pilot has a missile firing-quality solution against the enemy target, while an open triangle is not a firing-quality solution.

The pilot has a cursor on each screen, and can request the aircraft's avionics system to retrieve more information. The system can determine to a 98 percent probability the target's type of aircraft. If the system cannot make a solid identification to that degree, the aircraft is shown as an unknown.

One of the original objectives for the F-22 was to increase the percentage of fighter pilots that make "kills." The *inter/intraflight data link* (IFDL) is one of the most powerful tools that make all F-22s more capable. All Raptors can be linked together to trade information without radio calls with each one of the accompanying F-22s.

Each pilot is then free to operate more autonomously because, for example, the leader can tell at a glance what the wingperson's fuel state is, what weapons are remaining, and even the enemy aircraft targeted. Classic tactics based on visual "tallyho" (visual identification) and violent formation maneuvers that reduce the wing man to "hanging on" may have to be revised in the light of such capabilities.

Hands-on Throttle and Stick

Unlike most modern U.S. fighters, the F-22 has a hands-on throttle and stick (HOTAS) side-stick controller (similar to an F-16's) and two engine throttles. These are the aircraft's primary flight controls. The GEC-built stick is located on the right console, and there is a swing-out, adjustable armrest. The stick is force-sensitive and has a throw (travel range) of only about 3¼ in throughout its 360° circle of operation. The two F119 engine throttles are located on the left console.

Both the sidestick controller and the engine throttles are high-use controls during air combat. To support pilot functional requirements, the grips include buttons and switches that are both shape- and texture-coded to control more than 60 different time-critical functions. These buttons are used for controlling the offensive weapons targeting and release and defensive systems, although some of these, such as chaff and flares, can operate both automatically and manually.

Pilot Accommodations

Previous fighter cockpits were sized to accommodate the fifth percentile to 95th percentile pilots (a range of only 90 percent). The F-22 cockpit is sized to accommodate the 0.5 percentile to 99.5 percentile pilots (the body size of the central 99 percent of the USAF pilot population). This represents the largest range of pilots accommodated by any tactical fighter aircraft now in service. The rudder pedals are adjustable; and importantly, the pilot has 15° over-the-nose visibility as well as excellent over-the-side and aft visibility.

Lighting

The cockpit interior lighting is fully night-vision-goggle (NVG)-compatible, as is the exterior lighting. The cockpit panels feature extended life, self-balancing, electroluminescent (EL) edge-lit panels with an integral life-limiting circuit that runs the lights at the correct power setting throughout their life. It starts at half power and gradually increases the power output to ensure consistent panel light intensity over time. As one result, the cockpit always presents a well-balanced lighting system to the pilot. The panels produce low amounts of heat and power and are very reliable.

The aircraft also has integral position and anticollision lights (including strobes) on the wings. The low-voltage EL formation lights are located at critical positions for nighttime flying operations on the aircraft. These are located on either side of the forward fuselage section under the chine, on the tip of the upper left and right wings, and on the outside of both vertical stabilizers. There are similar air refueling lights on the butterfly doors that cover the air refueling receptacle.

Life Support Ensemble

The F-22's life support system (LSS) integrates all critical components of clothing, protective gear, and aircraft equipment necessary to sustain the pilot's life while flying the aircraft. In the past, these components had been designed and produced separately.

The Raptor's LSS components include

- An onboard oxygen-generating system (OBOGS) that supplies breathable air to the pilot

- An integrated breathing regulator/anti-*g* (BRAG) valve that controls flow and pressure to the facemask and pressure suit garments

- A chemical/biological/cold-water immersion (CB/CWI) protection ensemble

- An upper-body counterpressure garment and a lower body anti-*g* garment that acts as a partial-pressure suit at high altitudes

- An air-cooling garment, which will also be used by pilots on the U.S. Army's RAH-66 Comanche helicopter to provide thermal relief for the pilot

- Helmet and helmet-mounted systems, including chemical/biological (C/B) goggles and C/B hood, and the MBU-22/P breathing mask and hose system.

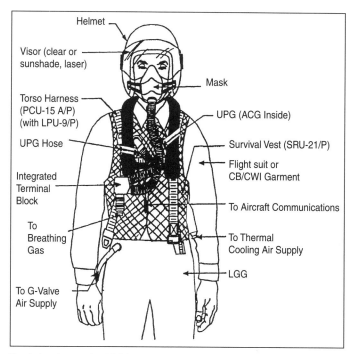

Back in the early 1940s, Northrop designed several fighter aircraft in which their pilots would lie prone to absorb a force as great as 12*g* during combat maneuvers. These never went into production, however. Seated upright, today's fighter pilots are expected to pull at least 9*g* during combat maneuvers. The F-22's Boeing-engineered life support system (LSS) is shown. *(Lockheed Martin Corporation.)*

The Boeing-led support system development and its suppliers designed the life support system with the F-22's advanced performance capabilities in mind. The separate components of the life support system must simultaneously meet pilot protection requirements established by the USAF in the areas of higher-altitude flight, acceleration, heat distress, cold-water immersion, C/B environments, fire, noise, and high-altitude/high-speed-speed ejection.

Emergency escape-system tests have demonstrated that the life support will protect pilots when exposed to wind speeds of up to 600 knots. Current life support systems are designed to provide protection only up to 450 knots. The head-mounted portions of the life support system are about 30 percent lighter than existing systems, which improves mobility and endurance time for pilots. With its advanced design, the HGU-86/P helmet that is used by F-22 pilots during EMD reduces the stresses on a pilot's neck by 20 percent during high-speed ejection compared to the current HGU-55/P helmets. The F-22 pilot's helmet fits more securely as the result of an ear cup tensioning device and is easily fitted to a pilot's head. The helmet provides improved passive noise protection and incorporates an active noise reduction system for superior pilot protection.

The aforementioned CB/CWI garment is to be worn by pilots when they fly over large bodies of cold water or into C/B warfare situations. These garments meet or exceed USAF requirements. During cold-water immersion tests, the body temperature of the test subjects wearing the garments fell no more than a fraction of a degree after sitting in nearly 32°F water for 2 hours. Current CWI suits allow body temperatures to drop below the minimum of the body's normal temperature of 98.6°F within 1½ hour.

Cockpit Canopy

The Raptor's cockpit canopy is about 140 in long, 45 in wide, and 27 in high, and weighs about 360 lb. It is of a rotate/translate design, which means that it comes down, slides forward, and locks in place with pins, and then reverses the process to open. The F-22's canopy is a much more complex piece of equipment that it would appear to be.

The F-22 canopy's transparency (made of Sierracine) features the largest piece of monolithic polycarbonate material formed today. It has no canopy bow, offers the pilot superior optics (zone 1 quality) throughout (not just in the area near the HUD), and offers the requisite stealth features.

The canopy is resistant to C/B and environmental agents, and has been successfully tested to withstand the impact of a 4-lb bird at 350 knots of indicated airspeed. It also protects the pilot from lightning strikes.

The ¾-in-thick polycarbonate transparency is actually made of 2⅜-in-thick sheets that are heated and fusion-bonded (the sheets actually meld to become a single-piece article) and then drape forged. The F-16's canopy, for comparison, is made up of laminated sheets. A laminated canopy generally offers better bird-strike protection, and because of the lower altitude where the F-16 operates, this is an advantage. However, lamination also adds weight as well as reduced optics.

As engineered, the chance of postejection canopy-seat-pilot collision is minimized as the F-22 canopy (with frame) weighs slightly more on one side than the other. When the canopy is jettisoned, the weight differential is enough to make it slice nearly 90° to the right as it clears the aircraft.

ACES II Ejection Seat

The F-22 employs an improved version of the Boeing (formerly McDonnell Douglas) ACES II (Advanced Concept Ejection Seat) emergency ejection seat that is used in nearly every other USAF jet-powered combat aircraft. The seat has a center mounted (between the pilot's legs) ejection control.

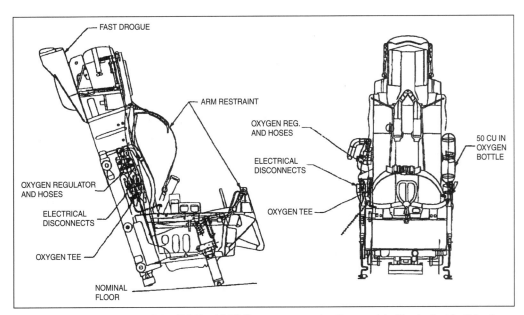

The right and back sides of the F-22's ACES II emergency ejection seat is illustrated in this drawing. (*Lockheed Martin Corporation.*)

The F-22 version of the Boeing-built ACES II includes several improvements over the previous ACES seat models. These improvements include:

- The addition of an active *arm restraint system* to eliminate arm-flail injuries during high-speed ejections.

- An improved *fast-acting seat stabilization drogue parachute* system to provide increased seat stability and safety for the pilot during high-speed ejections. The drogue 'chute is located behind the pilot's head, rather than at the rear of the seat, and is mortar-deployed.

- A new *electronic seat and aircraft sequencing system* that improves the timing of the various events that have to happen in order for the pilot to eject (initiation, canopy jettison, and seat catapult ignition).

- A *larger capacity oxygen bottle* that gives the ejecting pilot more breathing air to support ejection at higher altitudes (if required).

The F-22 ACES II ejection system uses the standard analog three-mode seat sequencer that automatically senses the seat speed and altitude, and then selects the proper mode for optimum seat performance and safe recovery of the pilot. Mode 1 is low speed, low altitude; mode 2 is high speed, low altitude; and mode 3 is high altitude.

The Armament System

> We want the other guy to quit in the bottom of the first inning and go home.
> **JEFF RHODES** *Lockheed Martin Aeronautical Systems*

The F-22 is a warbird, as its official name implies. Its weapons include the AIM-9M/-9X Sidewinder, the AIM-120C "Slammer," the GBU-32 Joint Direct Attack Munition (JDAM), and the M61A2 20-mm Vulcan cannon and, in addition, externally carried stores of many types.

The AIM-9M/-9X Sidewinder

On the F-22, a single AIM-9M/-9X Sidewinder is carried within each one of the Raptor's two side weapons bays, which are located on either side of the fuselage on the outside of the engine air inlets. The side bays are covered by two thermoset composite doors that run the length of the missile compartment and are hinged at the top and bottom of the bay.

The new version of the Sidewinder, the AIM-9X, is in development at this writing. It is to replace the AIM-9M variant. Although the AIM-9X is slightly longer than the AIM-9M, it will still fit in the F-22's side weapons bays without modification. The AIM-9X is to retain many of the earlier Sidewinder's capabilities while strengthening the design with airframe improvements and advanced seeker technology, including focal plane arrays, adaptive compensation techniques, and infrared (heat) signals processing.

The Raytheon/Loral AIM-9M is currently the only operational USAF variant of the Sidewinder. It has an all-aspect (any direction) intercept capability, improved defenses against infrared countermeasures, enhanced background discrimination capability, and a reduced-smoke rocket motor.

The AIM-9M is 9 ft, 5 in long with a diameter of 5 in. It has a fin span of 2 ft, 1 in and weighs 191 lb. Its maximum speed is more than Mn 2.0, with a range of more than 10 mi. It is supplied with a high explosive, blast fragmentation warhead that weighs 20.8 lb. It is powered by a single Thiokol Hercules Mk. 36 solid propellant rocket motor.

The Raytheon Company and Loral Autoneutronics–built AIM-9M is carried on a Lockheed Martin Tactical Aircraft Systems (LMTAS)-built LAU-141/A hydraulic launcher, called

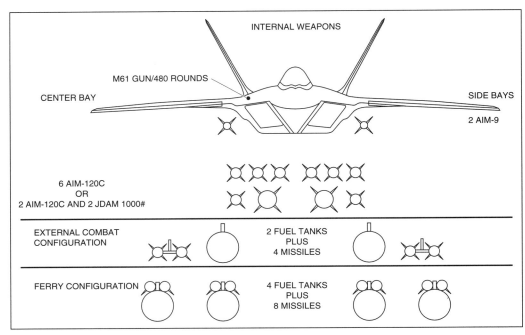

INTERNAL WEAPONS

M61 GUN/480 ROUNDS

CENTER BAY

SIDE BAYS

2 AIM-9

6 AIM-120C
OR
2 AIM-120C AND 2 JDAM 1000#

EXTERNAL COMBAT
CONFIGURATION

2 FUEL TANKS
PLUS
4 MISSILES

FERRY CONFIGURATION

4 FUEL TANKS
PLUS
8 MISSILES

An F-22 internal, external, and ferry weapons carriage capability is shown. The eight missiles in its ferry configuration cannot be fired. *(Lockheed Martin Corporation.)*

a *trapeze launcher*. This launcher, which uses some components from the existing LAU-128/A launcher, is basically the wingtip launch rail from an F-16 with a swing-out mechanism that extends rapidly. The LAU-141/A is also fitted with a missile motor plume deflector, which prevents damage to the side weapons bay as the missile launches off the rail.

Each Sidewinder is loaded by opening the F-22's side weapons bay doors, extending the trapeze launcher rail, sliding it onto the rail, retracting the missile, and closing the doors. Most Sidewinders are loaded manually, using a three-person load crew to evenly distribute the 191 lb of weight for each missile (about 63 lb for each person).

To launch a Sidewinder from an F-22, the side weapons bay doors open. After the doors open, the trapeze launcher, with missile attached, extends to put the missile's seeker into the slipstream. The missile's nose-mounted heat seeker acquires the target, after which the Sidewinder's rocket motor ignites and the AIM-9M/-9X flies of the rail. The trapeze launcher then retracts, and the weapons bay doors close. Once launched, the F-22 pilot can depart the area, as the Sidewinder is autonomous after it leaves the launch rail, following its seeker to the target. The entire Sidewinder launch sequence, from doors opened to doors closed, takes only a few seconds.

The AIM-120C "Slammer"

The Raptor's chief weapon is the radar-guided Hughes Missile Systems and Raytheon Company–built AIM-120C Advanced Medium-Range Air-to-Air Missile (AMRAAM), which is unofficially nicknamed "Slammer" by fighter pilots. It supplements, and in some cases, replaces the

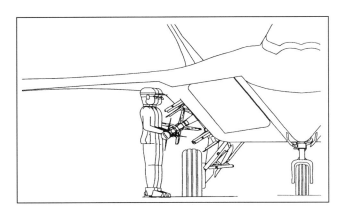

Using three ordnance technicians, an AIM-9 is loaded into the F-22's right-side weapons bay. One AIM-9 can be carried in weapons bays on either side. *(Lockheed Martin Corporation.)*

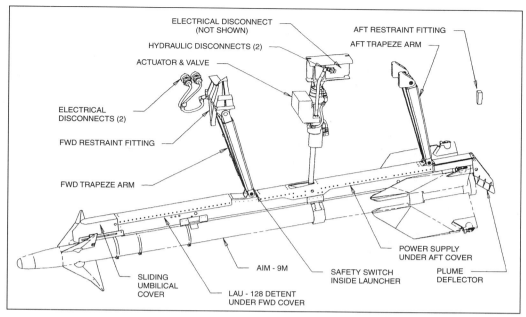

The LAU-141/A trapeze launcher is shown with an AIM-9 Sidewinder missile. *(Lockheed Martin Corporation.)*

Raytheon/Hughes AIM-7 Sparrow series of radar-guided air-to-air missiles which have been used since the late 1950s.

The AIM-120C provides all-weather, all-launch environment capability for the F-22, in addition to the USAF's F-15 Eagle and F-16 Fighting Falcon, the U.S. Navy's F-14 Tomcat, as well as the U.S. Navy's and U.S. Marines' F/A-18 Hornet.

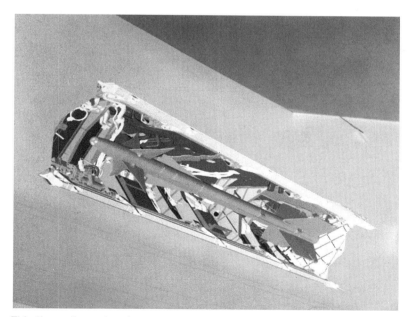

This three-dimensional, computer-generated rendering shows the left-side weapons bay of an F-22 with an AIM-9M Sidewinder loaded. The F-22 will also be compatible with the next-generation Sidewinder, the AIM-9X, which has been in development since mid-1995. *(Lockheed Martin Corporation.)*

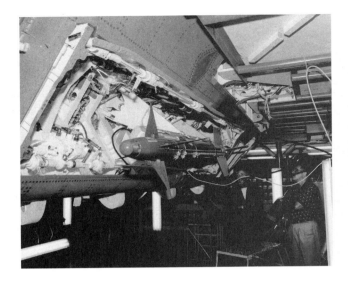

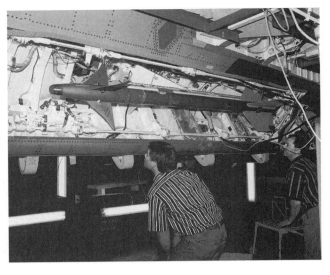

AIM-9 Sidewinder weapon-fit testing at LMTAS, Fort Worth, Texas. *(Lockheed Martin Corporation.)*

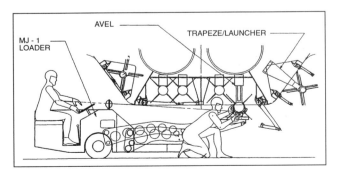

Using an MJ-1 loader, an AIM-120 is loaded into the F-22's main weapons bay. Up to six AIM-120s can be carried. *(Lockheed Martin Corporation.)*

This deadly missile features multiple target engagement capability, increased maximum launch range, a reduced-smoke rocket motor, and improved handling and maintenance qualities. The AMRAAM entered into development in 1981, and the 33rd Tactical Fighter Wing at Eglin AFB, Florida, was first to operate it in early 1990.

The AIM-120C "Slammer" is carried internally in the Raptor's main weapons bay, which is located on the undermost part of the fighter on centerline. The main bay is closed by a pair of thermoset composite bifold doors that open outward toward the F-22's wingtips. Depending on the mission requirement, two, four, or six AMRAAMs can be carried within the main bay.

Each AIM-120 is carried on an EDO Corporation–built LAU-142/A pneumatic-hydraulic AMRAAM Vertical Eject Launcher (AVEL). To minimize missile movement within the main weapons bay, AVELs are built to be strong and weigh just below 113 lb each. The AVEL, built mostly of aluminum alloy, has a 9-in stroke, and ejects a missile out of the bay at more than 25 feet per second (fps) with a force of $40g$ (40 times the force of gravity) at maximum acceleration. In addition, unlike prevailing missile launchers on other fighter aircraft, the LAU-142/A AVEL needs no pyrotechnics (explosive charges), and requires less logistics support than other launch systems.

The missiles are loaded from the opposite side of the F-22 Raptor fighter (missiles in the left side of the weapons bay are loaded from the right and vice versa), in order to clear the open main weapons bay doors. The current MJ-1 load vehicle (called a "jammer" or a "slammer" jammer) is used to load the AIM-120s into the F-22. The AMRAAMs are staggered within the bay to prevent fins on nearby missiles from clashing with each other when they are launched.

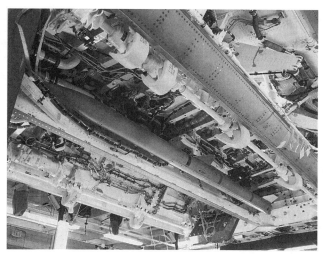

AIM-120 "Slammer" weapon-fit testing at LMTAS. *(Lockheed Martin Corporation.)*

Each AIM-120 receives target information from the F-22 prior to launch by way of a Military Standard (MIL-STD) 1760 data bus. Once launched, an AMRAAM can operate independently of the Raptor, as it has its own internal guidance system and an active radar, allowing the F-22 pilot to "launch and leave," that is, to fire a missile, or missiles, and leave the area, thus avoiding a close-in dogfight. In addition, a missile can receive midcourse target updates from the launch aircraft.

With the F-22's first-look, first-shoot, first-kill capability in any environment, the entire missile launch sequence—doors opened, AVEL ejecting the missile, missile ignition and flyaway, and doors closing—takes only a few seconds. This schedule holds true whether one, or as many as six, AMRAAMs are launched.

The AIM-120C AMRAAM has a high-explosive, direct-fragmentation warhead that weighs 48 lb. Its powerplant is a two-stage, solid propellant rocket motor provided by Aerojet. It is 12.0 ft long with 7 in diameter and has a finspan of 1 ft, 6 in. It weighs 345 lb, has a range of about 30 mi, and has an approximate Mn 4.0 cruise speed.

In a typical combat load, the F-22 carries six AIM-120Cs—three in each side of the main weapons bay, with the center missiles staggered ahead of the two inboard and two outboard missiles.

The GBU-32 Joint Direct Attack Munition (JDAM)

The Boeing GBU-32 JDAM is a tail guidance kit that converts existing unguided free-fall "dumb" bombs into near-precision-guided "smart" bombs. It also includes strap-on strakes that attach to the bomb's body for stability. It has no propulsion system.

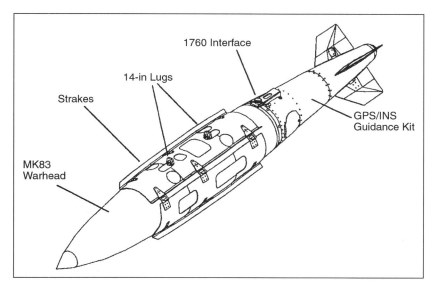

Two 1000-lb class GBU-32 JDAMs can be carried by an F-22. They are carried side by side within the Raptor's main weapons bay on EDO-built BRU-46/A bomb racks. *(Lockheed Martin Corporation.)*

Guided to its intended target by an Inertial Navigation System (INS)/Global Positioning (satellite) System (GPS), the GBU-32 has an approximate range of 15 mi. For the Raptor, the JDAM tail guidance kit is attached to the Mk. 83 1000-lb class conventional warhead bomb. The combined weight of the Mk. 83 bomb and the JDAM tail guidance kit is about 1015 lb. The JDAM gives the F-22 a highly accurate, autonomous, high-altitude all-weather conventional bombing capability.

The GBU-32 JDAM is carried only in the F-22's main weapons bay. Only two GBU-32s will be carried in this fashion, one inboard of either side of the main weapons bay as close to centerline as possible. When loaded with two GBU-32s, there is still enough room within the main weapons bay to carry two AIM-120s (one in either side of the bay), in addition to the AIM-9s carried in either side weapons bay. This means that even on a combat mission to attack ground targets, the Raptor retains significant air-to-air combat capability. There is a 2000-lb class GBU-31 JDAM, but the F-22 Raptor will carry only two of the 1000-lb class GBU-32s.

The M61A2 20-mm Vulcan Cannon

For close-in dogfighting capability, the F-22 is armed with a single, rotary-action, six-barrel, hydraulically operated 20-mm Gatling gun-type cannon. Built by General Dynamics Armament Systems, the Vulcan cannon is integrally mounted in the Raptor and is located on the right side of the aircraft between the top side of the wing root and fuselage. A gun door, located in the wing root area, is hydraulically controlled to open when firing the gun, which allows the 20-mm rounds and blast pressure to clear the muzzles. With a fixed forward-firing mount, the cannon has a 480-round closed-loop ammunition feed-storage subsystem housed integrally under the right wing root/fuselage for easy live ammunition upload and download of empty shell casings.

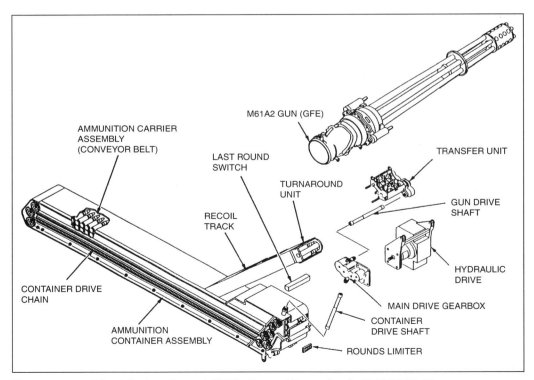

The government-furnished equipment (GFE), General Dynamics–built M-61A2 20-mm cannon system for the F-22. The cannon, called *Vulcan*, has been the mainstay of USAF cannon-armed fighters since the late 1950s. *(Lockheed Martin Corporation.)*

The Vulcan cannon system consists of the M61A2 gun, the Linear Linkless Ammunition Handling System (LLAHS), the hydraulic drive system, and the gun door/gun port–gas purge system. The cannon's maximum rate of fire is 6000 rounds per minute, and it has an effective range of several thousand yards. However, in actual close-in air-to-air combat, an F-22 pilot would most likely set the rate of fire at 100 rounds per minute. This much slower rate of fire gives the pilot a shot density to better enable a "kill," for with only 480 rounds available, the pilot can use the gun only five times per combat sortie.

The Raptor's M61A2 is a lightweight version of the M61A1, a proven gun, which has been in use since the late 1950s. It was first put into USAF service on another Lockheed fighter—the F-104 Starfighter.

The M61A2 is *government-furnished equipment* (GFE), that is, purchased by the government under separate contract and furnished to the F-22 contractor team. Power to operate the Vulcan cannon is provided by hydraulic pressure supplied by the raptor's hydraulic system. Each of the gun's six barrels fires only once during each revolution of the barrel cluster. The six rotating barrels—which have been machined down in thickness to decrease weight—contribute to long weapon life by minimizing barrel erosion and heat generation.

Externally Carried Stores

According to the USAF Air Combat Command, the F-22 Raptor is ranked as a multimission, air dominance fighter; that is, if properly modified and/or configured, it can carry and deliver just about anything in the U.S. arsenal. Much like its immediate predecessor, the F-15 Eagle, its external stores can range from the smallest conventional high-explosive warhead gravity bomb, to all types of air-to-air and air-to-ground missiles, to the highest yielding nuclear devices.

When used as a stealthy fighter-bomber—the USAF is not going to invest $60.8 billion (in fiscal year 1997 dollars) for 339 fighter aircraft that cannot double in brass as attack aircraft—the Raptor will strike surreptitiously. It will attack at relatively high speed, utilizing precision-guided munitions and smart bombs to hit tactical targets. For larger strategic targets, it can be equipped with advanced cruise-type missiles with nuclear warheads. However, a stealthy aircraft such as the F-22 will not be used for close support, where it would encounter all types of antiaircraft artillery and missile fire. Instead, it will be an elusive, quick-striking machine that unerringly hits its targets and then utilizes speed, stealth, and electronics to disappear.

The F-22's primary combat configuration is "clean," that is, with all its armament carried internally and no external stores. This is an extremely important factor in the Raptor's low-observable (stealth) characteristics. Moreover, it improves the aircraft's aerodynamics by dramatically reducing parasite drag, which, in turn, improves the F-22's maneuverability, range, and speed. Yet, if required, the Raptor can carry externally mounted stores.

The F-22 has four underwing hardpoints, each capable of carrying 5000 lb. A single-pylon design, which features forward and aft sway braces, an aft pivot, electrical connections, and fuel and air connections, is used on each hardpoint. Depending on the mission, either a jettisonable 600-gal external fuel tank or two pivot, so when stores are jettisoned, the forward attach point is released first, the pylon rotates on the pivot, and then the aft pivot is released. This action allows the pylon, along with the tank or launch rail, to clear the aircraft when it is released into the slipstream. Other components are

The BRU-47/A rack. The BRU-47/A rack is not the same type of rack that is used internally on the F-22 to carry the 1000-lb class GBU-32 JDAM, although they are similar and both are in use. There are no plans to carry GBU-32s externally on the Raptor, and the BRU-47/A is to be used only to hold an external fuel tank.

The LAU-128/A rail launcher. The LAU-128/A rail launcher is the standard rail launcher used today on the F-15 Eagle and can carry either of the missiles used on the F-22 Raptor: the AIM-9 Sidewinder or AIM-120 "Slammer." However, the two missiles carried on a rail launcher must be of the same type for F-22 aircraft weight and balance considerations.

The 600-gal fuel tank. The 600-gal fuel tank is similar to the same external tanks used on the current F-15 Eagle aircraft. However, a new tank is being developed that contains baffles to prevent the fuel from sloshing. This gives the tank better center of gravity (CG) control, which allows for safer jettisoning of the tanks.

The Radar System

A joint venture of Northrop Grumman's Electronic Sensors and Systems Division (ESSD) and Texas Instruments Incorporated is developing the advanced AN/APG-77 radar system for the F-22. The radar will give an F-22 pilot unprecedented capability in air-to-air combat, allowing the pilot to track, target, and shoot at multiple threat aircraft before the adversary's radar ever detects the Raptor.

The first AN/APG-77 radar system was in a Northrop Grumman rooftop testing laboratory in Baltimore, Maryland, where hardware and software integration took place as part of system-level tests. The radar tested was the first of nine systems delivered to the Lockheed Martin/Boeing team by the Northrop Grumman and Texas Instruments team as part of the EMD phase of the program.

The F-22A's radar system features an active, electronically scanned array antenna that operates in about 25 modes and provides the aircraft with long-range target acquisition, target track, and fire control capability. It features a separate transmitter and receiver for each of the antenna's radiating elements. This type of antenna provides the agility, low RCS, and wide bandwidth necessary to support the F-22's air dominance mission.

The first radar test flight took place on November 21, 1997, 3 weeks ahead of schedule, aboard the 757 FTB aircraft, configured to support F-22 integrated avionics flight-test activities.

The 757 FTB was operated out of Northrop Grumman ESSD's Baltimore facility in support of the F-22 radar engineering flight tests through the summer of 1998. It was later returned to Boeing's F-22 Avionics Integration Laboratory (AIL) in Seattle, Washington. At Boeing's AIL, the F-22 radar will be integrated with the avionics mission software and other aircraft avionics sensors such as the electronic warfare system and the communications, navigation, and identification system.

System integration and testing of the first F-22 radar lasted throughout 1997. As above, in late 1997, the radar was delivered to Boeing's F-22 Seattle AIL Laboratory, where engineers integrated the radar with other F-22 avionics. Additional EMD radar systems will be flight-tested on the 757 FTB and on F-22A flight-test aircraft.

The Northrop Grumman/Texas Instruments team completed about 75 percent of the EMD phase on schedule, within costs and meeting all performance requirements.

Full-scale production of the AN/APG-77 radar for the F-22 was scheduled to begin in mid- to late 1999.

The Landing and Arresting Gear

The Raptor uses a tricycle landing gear arrangement, with the standard two main landing gear assemblies (each with a single wheel) and a single-wheel, steerable nose landing gear assembly. The main landing gear retracts outward and upward into wells that are located in the midfuselage section and inboard wing sections. The nose landing gear retracts forward

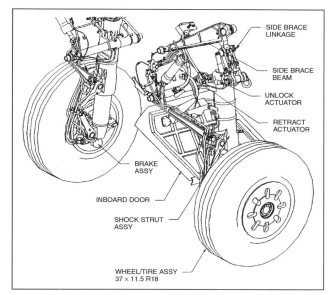

The F-22's main landing gear. *(Lockheed Martin Corporation.)*

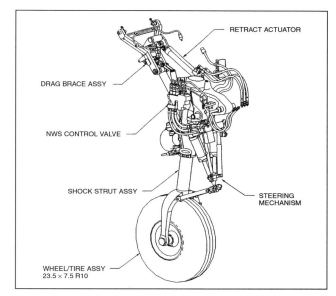

The F-22's nose landing gear. *(Lockheed Martin Corporation.)*

and up into the forward fuselage section on centerline. It should be noted that the YF-22A's nose gear retracted aft. This change of direction is to help eliminate possible foreign-object damage (FOD) to production F-22 engines.

The landing gear assemblies are made of AirMet 100 metal alloy, which provides greater strength and corrosion protection and are manufactured by Menasco. The main landing gears use a dual-piston design and are sized to withstand a collapsed gear or flat tire landing.

The Raptor's Allied Signal-built carbon brakes are always in antiskid mode, which means that the pilot has one less thing to remember to activate. The pilot applies pressure on the brakes by using the rudder pedals, but only after the F-22's weight-on-wheels sensor engages on landing.

The nose landing gear wheel is a *direct-drive system,* in which hydraulic force is applied to the nose wheel pivot to turn it. The nose gear is mechanically driven to align itself correctly before retraction.

As a safety precaution, the nose wheel clamshell doors and the lower inboard landing gear doors are physically linked to the landing gear itself. If an emergency extension (called *blowdown*) is required, the doors will be forced to open as the gear comes down. Also, the gear-down and locked indicators in the cockpit are battery-operated, so if all other systems malfunction, the pilot still has a way of knowing whether the landing gear is down and locked.

The three tires on the F-22 are Michelin Air-X steel-belted radials. Goodyear Bias-ply tires will also be qualified for the aircraft.

The F-22's landing gear doors are compatible with its low-observable design, and feature sawtoothed edges.

The F-22 has an arresting hook in an enclosed fairing that is located on the underside of aircraft on centerline. This hook, between the engines, is deployed in an emergency to stop the aircraft by means of hooking onto a wire cable strung out across the end of a runway. These barrier engagements work much like the arresting gear of an aircraft carrier.

While the Raptor has an arresting hook, it does not have the heavier structure necessary to withstand the stresses of a carrier landing. The shape of the arresting gear hook is not compatible with the aircraft's low-observable design, and thus requires a fairing and doors.

The Eagle Meets the Bird of Prey

The Lockheed Martin/Boeing F-22A Raptor will initially augment, and ultimately, super-sede the Boeing (formerly McDonnell Douglas) F-15 Eagle series of air superiority fighter aircraft. This is a challenging task. At this writing, and for a number of years to come, the F-15 Eagle is and probably will be the best operational fighter aircraft in the world. Nevertheless, the Raptor will be a worthy successor to the Eagle.

The YF-22A versus the F-15C in Mock Air-to-Air Combat

A simulated air-to-air combat exercise held in early 1991 pitted the YF119-powered YF-22A against an opposing F-15C Eagle near Edwards AFB. An Edwards-based F-15C, flown by a topnotch pilot, took on the YF119-powered YF-22A prototype. The actual re-sults remain classified. Raptor chief test pilot Paul Metz said: "In the end, we must demonstrate through actual test data that the production F-22 is at least twice as effec-tive as the current F-15 [C/D] models." Metz continued, "It is unfortunate that most of the work done to date [December 1997] remains classified but I can assure you that the Raptor's talons are far more deadly than two, four, or even 10 F-15s. It's that good." Metz added, "The secret of the F-22 lies as much in its computer power and stealth as it does in its ability to fly high and fast and 'turn on a dime.' While the first three Raptors will be basically engines and airframes, Raptors 04 through 09 will be full-up fighters with radar and all of the other sensors that comprise what's called a 'weapon system.' These later aircraft represent the F-22 as it will be flown by operational fighter pilots into the future."

At first glance, then, looking at the basic comparison matrix in Table 6-1, there do not ap-pear to be too many differences between the F-15C and the F-22A. While the F-22's maxi-mum speed and service ceiling numbers remain classified, one can logically assume that they equal or surpass those of the F-15. Since the F-22A's prototype. the YF-22A, is rumored

Operational since the early 1980s, the McDonnell Douglas (now Boeing) F-15C Eagle is currently the world's premier air superiority fighter. With its two very powerful P&W F100-PW-220 turbofan engines (about 23,500 lb thrust each), the F-15C has a thrust-to-weight ratio exceeding 1 : 1. Therefore, as shown here, an F-15C easily accelerates to beyond Mn 1.0 while climbing straight up. An F-15C from the Alaskan Air Command is freeze-framed in late 1983 as it zooms above Mt. McKinley, Alaska. *(McDonnell Douglas via AFFTC/HO.)*

to have totally outperformed an F-15C in the mock aerial dual, it is clear that the F-22A has a rate of climb, a roll rate, and maneuverability far superior to those of the F-15C.

F-22 Program Directors, Managers, and Vice Presidents

The Air Force Material Command (AFMC) Advanced Tactical Fighter (ATF)-cum-F-22 System Program Office at Wright-Patterson AFB, Ohio has had a number of directors since June 1983. In chronological order, these directors include Col. Albert Picarillo, June 1983 to December 1986; Col. (later Brig. Gen.) James A. Fain, December 1986 to June 1992; Brig. Gen. Robert F. Raggio, July 1992 to January 1996; and Brig. Gen. Michael C. Mushala, January 1996 to present.

In October 1985, Sherman A. Mullin became the ATF team program office vice president and general manager for Lockheed Aircraft Corporation (later Lockheed Martin Corporation) in Burbank and Palmdale, California. He served in this capacity until December 1990, when he became the third president of Lockheed's famed Skunk Works.

Raptor 01 on final approach to Dobbins ARB after its September 7, 1997 first flight. *(F-22 Team.)*

TABLE 6-1 Comparing the Warfighting Capabilities of the F-15C and the F-22A

	F-15C
Powerplant	Two afterburning Pratt & Whitney F100-PW-220 25,000-lb (11,250-kg) thrust class turbofan engines
Primary armament	One 20-mm M61A-1 cannon (940 rounds of ammunition), four AIM-7 or AIM-120, and four AIM-9 AAMs
Maximum speed	Mn 2.5+
Service ceiling	65,000 ft (19,697 m)
Length	63 ft, 9 in (19.43 m)
Height	18 ft, 8 in (5.69 m)
Wingspan	42 ft, 10 in (13.06 m)
	F-22A
Powerplant	Two afterburning Pratt & Whitney F119-PW-100 35,000-lb (15,890-kg) thrust class turbofan engines
Primary armament	One 20-mm M61A-2 cannon (480 rounds of ammunition), six AIM-120s, and two AIM-9 AAMs
Maximum speed	Mn 2.2+ (actual V_{max} is classified)
Service ceiling	50,000+ ft (15,240+ m) (actual ceiling is classified)
Length	62 ft, 1 in (18.9 m)
Height	16 ft, 5 in (5.0 m)
Wingspan	44 ft, 6 in (13.6 m)

The F-22A Raptor is shorter in length and height than either the F-15C or YF-22A. Its wing span at 44 ft, 6 in is greater than either one. Today's Raptor is very similar in size to yesterday's Eagle. *(Lockheed Martin Corporation.)*

Since December 1990, Lockheed Martin Aeronautical Systems has had several ATF program vice presidents and team program office general managers. These include James A. (Micky) Blackwell, December 1990 to April 1993; Gary A. Riley, April 1993 to November 1995; and C. T. (Tom) Burbage, November 1995 to present. Donald L. Herring became F-22 vice president and deputy team program office general manager for Lockheed Martin

At 64 ft, 2 in long, the YF-22A is 4 in shorter than an F-15C. Their respective wing spans are nearly identical: 43 ft, 0 in versus 42 ft, 9¾ in. *(Lockheed Martin Corporation.)*

The F-22 is widely regarded as the most advanced fighter in the world, combining a revolutionary leap in technology and capability with reduced support requirements and maintenance costs. It will replace the aging F-15C as America's front-line air superiority fighter, with deliveries to user squadrons beginning in 2002. *(Lockheed Martin Corporation.)*

The F-22 is designed to provide not just air superiority, but air dominance, winning quickly and decisively with few U.S. and allied casualties. The Raptor also has an inherent near-precision (later full-precision) air-to-ground capability. *(Lockheed Martin Corporation.)*

This is a quite dramatic view of Raptor 01 during its first flight. During the Raptor's public debut on April 9, 1997, Secretary of the Air Force Sheila Widnall said, "To a fighter pilot, quality of life is an F-22." She added, "This is a success story that is still a work in progress." *(F-22 Team.)*

The F-22A's combination of stealth, integrated avionics, maneuverability, agility, and supercruise capability will give Raptor pilots a first-see, first-fire, and first-destroy capability against aircraft of any potential enemy. *(Lockheed Martin Corporation.)*

Just before retracting its landing gear for the time in flight, Raptor 01 appears to be landing on the clouds. Raptor 02 joined 01 at Edwards in mid-1998, and has since enjoyed good flight-test activities. *(Lockheed Martin Corporation.)*

Aeronautical Systems in February 1994. Charla K. Wise is the vice president and program director for the F-22 program at Lockheed Martin Tactical Aircraft Systems in Fort Worth, Texas. She was formerly employed by LMTAS' predecessor, General Dynamics, and among many other assignments, became director of F-16 programs in 1987. The vice president and F-22 program manager for Boeing Defense and Space Group is Robert D. Barnes. Since February 1997, Barnes has been responsible for Boeing work on the F-22.

The Raptor's twin outward-canted vertical stabilizers are required for its stability at very high speeds. Although the F-22's maximum speed is classified, it probably matches the F-15C's announced maximum speed of Mn 2.5. *(F-22 Team.)*

Test pilot Paul Metz shuts down Raptor 01 after its first test hop. *(F-22 Team.)*

Paul Metz is seen seated beneath the F-22's large all-around-view cockpit canopy. Note the width of the F-22's instrument panel. *(F-22 Team.)*

Paul Metz gives the thumbs-up sign as he egresses Raptor 01 after its very successful first flight. *(F-22 Team.)*

Excellent in-flight view of Raptor 01 shows off its sporty lines. *(F-22 Team.)*

At Pratt & Whitney Large Military Engines in West Palm Beach, Florida, Walter N. (Walt) Bylciw has been senior vice president of the F119 program, since June 1995. In 1998, he became vice president of the P&W F119 program. He was preceded by Gary Plourde who was F119 program manager from May 1983 to May 1985; Plourde led the PW5000 demonstration program that led to the YF119.

The F-22's instrument panel is complex. *(F-22 Team.)*

Mission: Possible

The Lockheed Martin Boeing F-22A represents the culmination of years of fighter development that began with the first indigenous U.S. fighter design to reach production, the Thomas Morse MB-3, a biplane fighter of 1918. The Thomas-Morse was succeeded by a brilliant series of fighters, each one incorporating modern developments. In the process there were aircraft that were clearly defined as being leaps ahead of their predecessors. The North American F-86 was such an advance over the Lockheed P-80, and the McDonnell F-4 was similarly a leap forward over the North American F-100. However, no previous aircraft had yet superseded an airplane with such outstanding and still world-class characteristics as those of the Boeing (formerly McDonnell Douglas) F-15 Eagle. Fortunately, the Raptor has the necessary performance and equipment to do just that.

The F-22 Mission

When it becomes operational in 2005, the F-22A's primary objective will be to establish absolute control of the skies through the conduct of counterair operations. The F-22A will

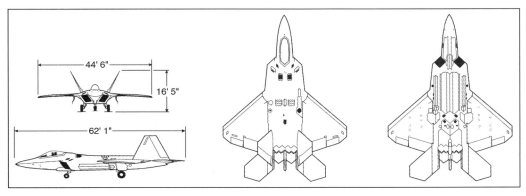

This four-view of the F-22A Raptor shows its flight control surfaces, side and main weapons bays, and landing gear doors, among other things. *(Lockheed Martin Corporation.)*

The F-22 team logo. *(F-22 Team.)*

Displaying its Spirit of America logo, Raptor 01 is towed to the flight line after its April 9, 1997 rollout ceremony. Armed with a 20-mm cannon and up to eight AAMs carried internally, and another four to eight AAMs carried externally, the Raptor will indeed be a dedicated bird of prey. *(Lockheed Martin Corporation.)*

also have a precision ground strike capability. It will be able to defeat threats that the F-15 would no longer be able to counter, by means of its increased speed and range, enhanced offensive and defensive avionics, and much reduced observability.

The F-22's design also emphasizes reliability and maintainability of its systems to achieve its intended mission-capable rate. Operational Raptor squadrons will appreciate its projected 95 percent or higher mission-capable rate, which will ensure that aircraft will be immediately available for subsequent combat missions.

Another view of Raptor 01 as it is towed to the LMAS flight line at Dobbins ARB in Marietta, Georgia. *(Lockheed Martin Corporation.)*

After retracting its landing gear for the first time in flight, EMD F-22A number one flies at 10,000 ft above the state of Georgia. One Raptor test pilot, USAF Lt. Col. Steve Rainey, said, "It's the best flying aircraft I have flown, and it sets a new standard of excellence in fighter aviation." *(Lockheed Martin Corporation.)*

Who Will Operate the F-22 Raptor

Two of the first outfits to get F-22s will be the 79th Test and Evaluation Group at Eglin AFB, Florida, and the 412th Test Squadron at Edwards AFB in California. These units will be responsible for the ongoing test and evaluation processes associated with the Raptor's flying and fighting tactics and its weapons systems and weapons delivery techniques.

Although no actual beddown assignments have been made at this writing, the 1st Fighter Wing and its three fighter squadrons (the 27th, 71st, and 94th) at Langley AFB, Virginia, will most probably receive the first operational F-22As. The next two might be the 33rd Fighter Wing and 53rd Wing at Eglin AFB in Florida.

Other possible F-22 user candidates include the 3rd Wing, Elmendorf AFB, Alaska; 18th Fighter Wing, Kadena Air Base, Japan; 48th Fighter Wing, Royal Air Force or RAF Lakenheath, England; 52nd Fighter Wing, Spangdahlem Air Base, Germany; and the 366th Wing, Mountain Home AFB, Idaho.

Building the F-22

The number of manufacturing processes required for the completion of each F-22A Raptor is astonishing. Lockheed Martin said it best: "If building an aircraft that has been described as 'the only thing more complex than a human body' in five separate geographic locals wasn't challenging enough, the F-22 team also had to build an aircraft to tolerances on the order of ten-thousandths of an inch in order to meet its stealth requirements."

When the first EMD F-22A's fuselage was mated in the fall of 1996, the computer-designed pieces went to-

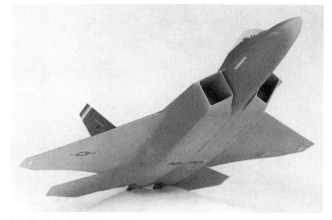

Marked in the USAF ACC's 1st Fighter Wing colors (tail code FF), a ½₀-scale model shows off the aircraft's large, outward-canted engine air inlets. *(Lockheed Martin Corporation.)*

From about 15 mi away, an F-22 sends one of its two GBU-32 JDAMs on its way toward a predetermined target. With a CEP of only about 6 m 234 in, the satellite-guided JDAM is an extremely lethal weapon. *(Lockheed Martin Corporation.)*

gether just as the designers had predicted. In the final assembly, the forward fuselage that was made in Marietta was mated to the middle fuselage made in Fort Worth, and that mid-fuselage was mated to the aft fuselage made in Seattle, and all this took only a few days to accomplish. The first set of wings was mated in less than 48 hours. The vertical tailplanes went on in less than a day.

The integrated product team (IPT) philosophy under which the F-22 airframe and F119 powerplant are being developed has paid big dividends in the manufacturing area. Be-

This artist's concept of Raptor state of the art in July 1997 depicts Paul Metz in Raptor 01. *(Lockheed Martin Corporation.)*

tween the two body mates and the wing joins, only 40 shims had to be generated, all about the thickness of a sheet of paper.

CATIA and COMOK

The computer revolution has changed the detail design process of the aircraft. With the IBM/Dassault Systems–designed *computer-aided, three-dimensional interactive application* (CATIA), the aircraft designer can design the parts of the F-22 as a solid object, not merely lines on a flat page.

With COMOK (a team-developed computer mockup simulation), the designer can visualize every aspect of the design, including complex routing for wires, tubes, and cables. The tremendous computer capability meant that no full-scale engineering mockup was required for the F-22, saving thousands of worker-hours and perhaps millions of dollars.

These advanced computer programs allow the design engineer and the manufacturing engineer actual look-sees inside the structure before it is built. More than simply a visualization, the computer data that creates these images are precisely stored design measurements that can be transferred, again by computers, between the team's many locations, in Marietta, Georgia; Fort Worth, Texas; Seattle, Washington; West Palm Beach, Florida; East Hartford, Connecticut; and to supplier locations throughout the nation.

Parts of the aircraft fit remarkably well when received in Marietta, where final assembly takes place, even though no master tool was sent to trial-fit the pieces. More than 270 mas-

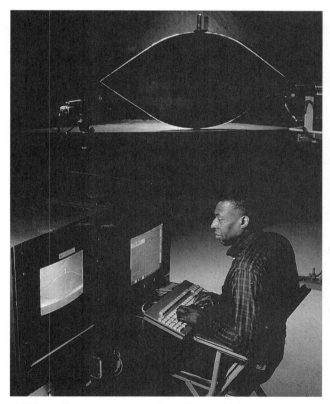

LMAS quality assurance engineer Bryant McKee uses an advanced optical contour measurement system to examine and quantify surface variances of a test panel on May 15, 1996 that is representative of an F-22 forward fuselage section. *(Lockheed Martin Corporation.)*

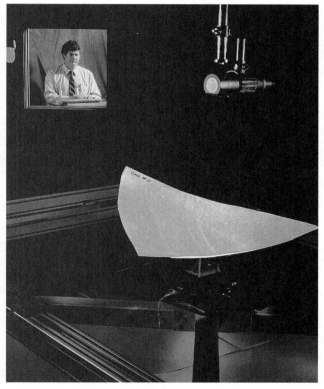

From the X (x-ray) files, LMAS quality assurance engineer Dave van Proyen uses an advanced x-ray system in May 1996 to measure porosity in an aircraft part made of composite material. This new device, called the *energy-sensitive x-ray system,* uses an x-ray tube source (suspended above) with an eight-channel, energy-sensitive detector located below the part. *(Lockheed Martin Corporation.)*

In a demonstration of a tool that will be very important in the assembly of F-22s, LMAS' Bryant McKee inspects the gap between the avionics bay access door and the forward fuselage of the YF-22A ATF prototype, circa early 1996. *(Lockheed Martin Corporation.)*

ter tools have been eliminated as confidence in the three-dimensional tools grew. Amazingly, as part of the IPT process, the team found that it could hold tolerances to $\frac{1}{6000}$ in on parts.

Aircraft Materials Composition

The aft fuselage section of the F-22 consists of mostly high-strength titanium alloys, as it has to hold the Raptor's F119 engines, and it must be able to withstand the tremendously high temperatures that the engines create. The middle fuselage section transitions from titanium (in the larger, load-bearing bulkheads) to forged aluminum bulkheads and aluminum frames. The forward fuselage section contains a composite fuel tank (behind the pilot's ACES II ejection seat) and is made of machined aluminum. The wings are made of composite spars and skins with titanium reinforcement.

Final Assembly

Final assembly operations for the air dominance fighter take place in the 3.5-million-sq-ft B-1 building at LMAS' Marietta facility. However, other things necessary for the F-22A specifically take place in nearby facilities. These include composite parts fabrication, painting, radar cross-section (RCS) verification, ground-based engine runs, and flight operations.

RCS Verification Facility The largest of the newly constructed facilities at Marietta is the RCS verification building. This 50,000 sq-ft fully enclosed structure is used to test the "stealthiness" of each F-22 when it comes off the assembly line.

The main section of this building features a 45-ft-diameter turntable with precise positioning capability that allows for testing of finished Raptors. The facility has a separate 60-by-210-ft anechoic chamber for aircraft antenna testing.

How Many F-22s Will Be Built

At this writing, because of ever-increasing costs for new and advanced military aircraft—especially bombers and fighters—and the "peace is breaking out all over" philosophy, the USAF plans to procure 339 F-22s through the year 2011. Specifically, this means a total purchase of nine EMD aircraft, two PRTV aircraft, six initial production aircraft, and 322 full-production aircraft.

In July 1998 the USAF awarded the Lockheed Martin/Boeing team two contracts totaling up to $70.7 million for advanced procurement and program support for two F-22A production representative test vehicles or (PRTVs). These contracts, valued at up to $2.1 billion, include options for the two PRTVs and for the first six initial production (IP) F-22As. Therefore, at this writing, 17 Raptors are on order: nine EMD F-22As, two PRTV F-22As, and six IP F-22As.

"These contracts lead us from EMD into production, and bring to fruition months of hard work by the entire F-22 team, including contractors and the U.S. Air Force," said Tom Burbage, F-22 general manager and LMAS F-22 program vice president. "Drafting perfor-

Machinist Mike Osborne, Boeing Defense and Space Group manufacturing, uses a horizontal-boring mill to cut part of an F-22 aft fuselage frame in February 1995. A week earlier, the air vehicle Critical Design Review, a major milestone, was completed. *(The Boeing Company.)*

mance-based contracts while still producing and testing EMD aircraft brought a special challenge."

The contract for PRTV F-22A long-lead materials includes not-to-exceed options for PRTV full award and Lot 1 advance procurement for six IP aircraft that came about in December 1998, and Lot 1 full award scheduled for December 1999.

Boeing uses advanced processes to build wing skins for the F-22. Agnes Ulrich, Boeing plastic bench mechanic, monitors an automated contour tape-laying machine that applies layers of advanced composite resin-impregnated tape on top of a precisely curved surface to form a wing skin. Automated fabrication replaces the conventional and labor-intensive hand-layup method. *(The Boeing Company.)*

At this writing, then, in addition to the nine EMD F-22As, the USAF plans to buy the two PRTV aircraft and 12 production lots totaling 339 F-22 aircraft, at an estimated cost of $34.7 billion in fiscal year 1998 dollars.

How the Raptor Is Expected to Perform When It Becomes Operational

Air superiority is the prerequisite for success in all our military operations: on land, at sea and in the air.

GENERAL RICHARD E. HAWLEY

The primary mission of the F-22 Raptor, fully armed with eight air-to-air missiles and its built-in 20-mm cannon, is air dominance. It is to gain and maintain complete air superiority throughout the entire theater of operations. Although air dominance is the F-22's chief mission, it has a built-in secondary air-to-ground capability. In this scenario, loaded with two satellite-guided GBU-32 JDAMs, its air-to-air missiles, and its onboard 20-mm cannon, it can destroy two ground installations and still be able to engage and destroy enemy fighters.

The F-22 could also serve in the so-called wild weasel role. Armed with two AGM-88 high-speed antiradiation missiles (HARMs), a single F-22 could take out at least two ground radar installations while maintaining its fighting capabilities.

For prestrike targeting information and poststrike bomb damage assessment (BDA), F-22s could be fitted with special equipment pods for high-speed photographic reconnaissance and mapping duties. Although there are no announced plans to create any reconnaissance fighter or RF-22 aircraft, the Raptor could easily perform the reconnaissance role.

The F-22 Raptor will be a multiple-mission aircraft. Whether intercepting bombers, fighting fighters, photographing or decimating ground-based facilities, it will be one very deadly warbird.

The Future

T he future of the F-22 Raptor largely depends on its ability to fly and fight like no other fighter aircraft in the world—to be the best of the best. To do this, in part, it must rely heavily on its low observable, or stealth, attributes.

In December 1977 and July 1978, Have Blue 1001 and 1002 made their respective first flights. Built by Lockheed Martin's famed Skunk Works, these Experimental Survivable Technology or XST models represented low observable or stealth aircraft. Following 88 flight tests between them (36 for XST-1 and 52 for XST-2), the USAF was convinced that stealth would work. The immediate result was the Lockheed Martin F-117 Nighthawk—the world's first, and still only, operational stealth light-attack fighter-bomber. *(Lockheed Martin Corporation.)*

The USAF/DARPA Have Blue competition boiled down to an entry from Lockheed and another from Northrop. Both firms built pole-mounted models that were thoroughly tested on radar ranges. *(Northrop Grumman Corporation via Chris Wamsley.)*

Stealth

The Lockheed Martin/Boeing F-22A Raptor is a fifth-generation operational stealth aircraft. It was preceded by the Lockheed Martin Skunk Works SR-71 Blackbird and its A-12/M-12/YF-12/D-21 predecessors, the Have Blue and Tacit Blue prototypes, the Lockheed Martin F-117 Nighthawk, and the Northrop Grumman B-2A Spirit.

The F-22 is a dedicated low-observable, or stealth, fighter aircraft and is optimized to take full advantage of this highly successful and combat-proven technology. At first glance, the Raptor shows its association with the basic shaping standards of a stealthy aircraft configuration. The leading and trailing edges of its wings and tailplanes have matching sweep angles (a design technique called *planform alignment*). Its fuselage and cockpit canopy employ oblique lines. The access panels, weapons bays doors, landing gear wells doors, cockpit canopy-to-fuselage junction, and other surface interfaces have sawtoothed or radically sloping lines. The twin vertical stabilizer tails are canted outward. The faces of the Raptor's twin F119 engines are deeply hidden by a pair of serpentlike air inlet ducts. Its weapons, during actual combat conditions, are carried internally rather than externally. Not surprisingly, shaping alone provides up to 85 percent of an aircraft's stealth requirements. The remaining 15 or so percent is accomplished through radar-absorbing material (RAM), radar-absorbing structure (RAS), and other classified means.

After Lockheed had successfully demonstrated that its XST aircraft could actually fly, and fly undetected by the best radar systems available, it won a contract to build five full-scale development and 59 production F-117A stealth fighters. As the star aircraft of Operation Desert Storm, the F-117 thoroughly proved that stealth worked. An F-117A (number 816) of the 49th Fighter Wing, Seventh Fighter Squadron is shown. *(Lockheed Martin Corporation.)*

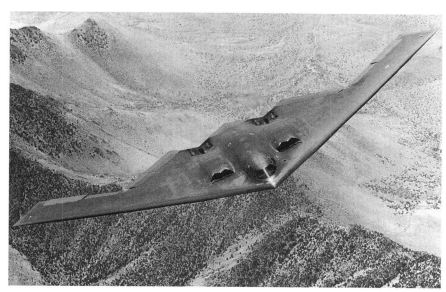

The fourth generation of stealth aircraft, the Northrop Grumman B-2A Spirit uses a different approach to obtain its low observability. Instead of the F-117's faceted approach, it employs an all-flying wing configuration, numerous compound curves, and rounded edges to accomplish its stealth capability. *(Boeing Airplane Company.)*

The following article was written by Alan Brown, who retired as director of engineering at Lockheed Corporate Headquarters in 1991. He is generally regarded as one of the founding fathers of stealth, or low-observable technology. Mr. Brown served a number of years as director of low observables technology at Lockheed Aeronautical Systems Company in Marietta, Georgia. From 1978 to 1982, he was the program manager and chief engineer for the F-117 stealth fighter and had been active in stealth programs since 1975. This article appeared in 1992, and part of it is excerpted below.

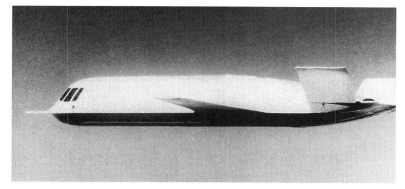

Another type of stealth aircraft was the Northrop Tacit Blue (Whale), which was created to demonstrate that a low observable surveillance aircraft with a low probability of intercept radar and other sensors could operate close to the forward line of battle with a high degree of survivability. The Tacit Blue Technology Demonstration Program ran from 1978 to 1985. Only one of these aircraft was built for flight-test activities, and it made 135 flights over a 3-year period. *(Northrop Grumman Corporation.)*

Enter the fifth-generation stealth aircraft, the first EMD F-22A Raptor, shown shortly after it received its multihued gray paint job and just before its public debut. As the F-22 is of about the same size and weight as the F-15C Eagle, its low observability makes it much more survivable than its forerunner. *(Lockheed Martin Corporation.)*

The premier USAF, Lockheed Martin, Boeing, and Pratt & Whitney EMD F-22A Raptor is shown at its April 9, 1997 unveiling at Marietta, Georgia. Named *Spirit of America* and dubbed *Raptor 01,* the first of nine EMD F-22s made a grand entry. *(Lockheed Martin Corporation.)*

Originally scheduled to fly in May 1997, and after several delays because of various minor problems, the premier Raptor made its maiden flight on September 7, 1997. Piloted by Lockheed Martin chief F-22 pilot Paul Metz, Raptor 01 took to the air at 10:18 A.M. local time for a successful first flight. *(Lockheed Martin Corporation.)*

Fundamentals of Stealth Design

Design for low observability, and specifically for low radar cross section (RCS), began almost as soon as radar was invented. The predominantly wooden de Havilland Mosquito was one of the first aircraft to be designed with this capability in mind.

Against World War II radar systems, that approach was fairly successful, but it would not be appropriate today. First, wood and, by extension, composite materials, are not transparent to radar, although they may be less reflective than metal; and second, the degree to which they are transparent merely amplifies the components that are normally hidden by the outer skin. These include engines, fuel, avionics packages, electrical and hydraulic circuits, and people.

In the late 1950s, radar-absorbing materials were incorporated into the design of otherwise conventionally designed aircraft. These materials had two purposes: to reduce the aircraft cross section against specific threats, and to isolate multiple antennas on aircraft to prevent cross talk. The Lockheed U-2 reconnaissance airplane is an example in this category.

By the 1960s, sufficient analytical knowledge had disseminated into the design community that the gross effects of different shapes and components could be assessed. It was quickly realized that a flat plate at right angles to an impinging radar wave has a very large radar signal, and a cavity, similarly located, also has a large return.

Thus, the inlet and exhaust systems of a jet aircraft would be expected to be dominant contributors to radar cross section in the nose-on and tail-on viewing directions, and the vertical tail dominates the side-on signature.

Airplanes could now be designed with appropriate shaping and materials to reduce their radar cross sections, but as good numerical design procedures were not available, it was unlikely that a completely balanced design would result. In other words, there was always likely

Near Edwards AFB in September 1998, Raptor 02 is shown on a test hop. With more than 70,000 total pounds of engine thrust, thrust-vectoring exhaust nozzles, close-coupled stabilators, and numerous other advanced aerodynamic features, operational F-22s will outperform any other fighter aircraft in the world. *(Lockheed Martin Corporation.)*

to be a component that dominated the return in a particular direction. This was the era of the Lockheed SR-71 "Blackbird."

Ten years later, numerical methods were developed that allowed a quantitative assessment of contributions from different parts of a body. It was thus possible to design an aircraft with a balanced radar cross section and to minimize the return from dominant scatterers. This approach led to the design of the Lockheed F-117A and Northrop B-2 stealth aircraft.

Over the past 15 [now 22] years there has been continuous improvement in both analytical and experimental methods, particularly with respect to integration of shaping and materials. At the same time, the counterstealth faction is developing and increasing understanding of its requirements, forcing the stealth community into another round of improvements. The message is, that with all the dramatic improvements of the last two decades, there is little evidence of leveling off in capability. This article, consequently, must be seen only as a snapshot in time.

Radar Cross-Section Fundamentals

There are two basic approaches to passive radar cross section reduction: shaping to minimize backscatter, and coating for energy absorption and cancellation. Both of these approaches have to be used coherently in aircraft design to achieve the required low observable levels over the appropriate frequency range in the electromagnetic spectrum.

Shaping

There is a tremendous advantage to positioning surfaces so that radar wave strikes them at close to tangential angles and far from right angles to edges, as will now be illustrated.

To a first approximation, when the diameter of a sphere is significantly larger than the radar wavelength, its radar cross section is equal to its geometric frontal area.

The return of a one-square-meter sphere is compared to that from a one-meter-square plate at different look angles. One case to consider is a rotation of the plate from normal incidence to a shallow angle, with the radar beam at right angles to a pair of edges. The other is with the radar beam at 45 degrees to the edges.

The frequency is selected so that the wavelength is about $\frac{1}{10}$ of the length of the plate, in this case very typical of acquisition radars on surface-to-air missile systems.

At normal incidence, a flat plate acts like a mirror, and its return is 30 decibels (dB) above (or 1,000 times) the return from the sphere. If we now rotate the plate about one edge so that the edge is always normal to the incoming wave, we find that the cross section drops by a factor of *1,000*, equal to that of the sphere, when the look angle reaches 30 degrees off normal to the plate.

As the angle is increased, the locus of maxima falls by about another factor of 50, for a total change of 50,000 from the normal look angle.

Now if you go back to the normal incidence case and rotate the plate about a diagonal relative to the incoming wave, there is a remarkable difference. In this case, the cross section drops by 30 dB when the plate is only eight degrees off normal, and drops another 40 dB by the time the plate is at a shallow angle to the incoming radar beam. This is a total change in radar cross section of 10,000,000!

From this, it would seem that it is fairly easy to decrease the radar cross section substantially by merely avoiding obviously high-return shapes and attitude angles.

However, multiple-reflection cases have not yet been looked at, which change the situation considerably. It is fairly obvious that energy aimed into a long, narrow, closed cavity, which is a perfect reflector internally, will bounce back in the general direction of its source. Furthermore, the shape of the cavity downstream of the entrance clearly does not influence this conclusion.

However, the energy reflected from a straight duct will be reflected in one or two bounces, while that from a curved duct will require four or five bounces. It can be imagined that with a little skill, the number of bounces can be increased significantly without sacrificing aerodynamic performance. For example, a cavity might be designed with a high-cross-sectional aspect ratio to maximize the length-to-height ratio. If we can attenuate the signal to some extent with each bounce, then clearly there is a significant advantage to a multibounce design. The SR-71 inlet follows these design practices.

However, there is a little more to the story than just the so-called ray tracing approach. When energy strikes a plate that is smooth compared to wavelength, it does not reflect totally in the optical approximation sense, i.e., the energy is not confined to a reflected wave at a complementary angle to the incoming wave.

The radiated energy, in fact, takes a pattern like a typical reflected wave structure. The width of the main forward scattered spike is proportional to the ratio of the wavelength to the dimension of the radiating surface, as are the magnitudes of the secondary and tertiary spikes. The classical optical approximation applies when this ratio approaches zero. Thus, the backscatter—the energy radiated directly back to the transmitter, increases as the wavelength goes up, or the frequency decreases.

When designing a cavity for minimum return, it is important to balance the forward scatter associated with ray tracing with the backscatter from interactions with the first surfaces. Clearly, an accurate calculation of the total energy returned to the transmitter is very complicated, and generally has to be done on a supercomputer.

Coatings and Absorbers

It is fairly clear that although surface alignment is very important for external surfaces and [engine air] inlet and [engine] exhaust [nozzle] edges, the return from the inside of a cavity is heavily dependent on attenuating materials. It is noted that the radar-frequency range of interest covers between two and three orders of magnitude. Permeability and dielectric constant are two properties that are closely associated with the effectivity of an attenuating material.

They both vary considerably with frequency in different ways for different materials. Also, for a coating to be effective, it should have a thickness that is close to a quarter wavelength at the frequency of interest.

High Temperature Coatings

Reduction of radar cross section of engine [exhaust] nozzles is also very important, and is complicated by high material temperatures. The electromagnetic design requirements for coatings are not different from those for low temperatures, but structural integrity is a much bigger issue.

Summary

The low signatures achieved by modern special-purpose aircraft are due to a combination of shaping, material, material selection, and careful attention to detail design. Budgeting of component signatures across a wide range of frequencies and attitude angles is mandatory. Just as in a blackout, the game can be given away by one chink of light.

The Future of the F-22

The future of the F-22 Raptor looks very bright, indeed, if predicated on the demonstrated performance of the aircraft. No other country currently has the capability to create an aircraft with the F-22's capabilities, and it is not obvious whether any will have such capability in the future. However, the continuing decline in military budgets might result in a reduction in the total number of F-22s to be produced. This, combined with the inevitable attrition of operational use, might mean that as advanced as the F-22 is, it will not be available in sufficient quantity to meet worldwide threats.

The F-22 is destined to be the world's air dominance fighter. While the more capable world nations strive to design, develop, and produce the Raptor's equals, the F-22 will undergo continuous upgrading to maintain its status. (Lockheed Martin Corporation.)

Lockheed Martin and Boeing are in the process of building and flying what could be called the sixth-generation stealth aircraft: the Joint Strike Fighter (JSF). Each firm is to build and fly two versions of the JSF. At this writing, Boeing's two JSF demonstrators—designated X-32A and X-32B—and Lockheed Martin's two JSF demonstrators—designated X-35A and X-35B—are to fly sometime in 2000. One X-32 and one X-35 will be capable of vertical and short takeoffs and landings, while one X-32 and one X-35 will make conventional takeoffs and landings. This artist's concept shows a Lockheed Martin conventional takeoff and landing version in USAF 20th Fighter Wing of Shaw AFB, South Carolina markings. *(Lockheed Martin Corporation.)*

The vertical and short takeoff and landing (V/STOL) version of the Lockheed Martin JSF is shown here in U.S. Marine Corps dress. Whichever version of the V/STOL JSF wins a production contract, it is to ultimately replace the USMC's Boeing AV-8B Harrier II—the famed Jump Jet. *(Lockheed Martin Corporation.)*

Conclusion

As brilliant as the McDonnell Douglas (now Boeing) F-15 design was, the passage of time has seen the emergence of a number of fighters with the capability to successfully engage it in combat. Because it lacks stealth capability, the F-15 is vulnerable to missile attack from fighters. In a situation in which the rules of engagement delay the F-15's attack, or in which the hostile fighters fire missiles from the front quadrant, the F-15s could lose the air battle. At best, they will have to fight a battle of attrition—and the United States, as a superpower should not have to engage in such combat. Foremost among the foreign fighters with significant capability to engage the F-15 successfully are the Mikoyan Gurevich MiG-29 Fulcrum and Sukhoi Su-27 Flanker. In addition, Russia continues to create new and advanced fighter aircraft, including the the Sukhoi Su-30MK, Sukhoi Su-37, and an experimental forward-swept wing Sukhoi fighter. All of these have some stealth characteristics.

Several excellent foreign fighter aircraft are also scheduled for production. These include the Alenia/British Aerospace/CASA/Daimler-Benz Eurofighter Typhoon, the Dassault Aviation/Snecma/Thomson-CSF

Shadowed by two World War II–era North American P-51D Mustangs, a pair of USAF Boeing JSFs are on the prowl. In November 1996, the U.S. Department of Defense awarded Boeing a contract to proceed with the 51-month Concept Demonstration Phase (CDP) of the JSF program. *(The Boeing Company.)*

Carrying ten 500-lb class bombs each, two USMC Boeing JSFs come on shore to attack an undisclosed target. Escorted by two WW-II era Chance Vought F4U Corsairs, these two JSFs are coming in fast and low. *(The Boeing Company.)*

Using its stealth capability to full advantage, in this artist's concept, an F-22 has just released both of its 1000-lb class GBU-32 JDAMs from its main weapons bay. The GBU-32 is a near-precision standoff weapon guided to its target by means of an inertial measurement unit updated in flight with data from Global Positioning System (GPS) satellites. *(Lockheed Martin Corporation.)*

In this artist's concept of a USAF 366th Wing F-22 from Mountain Home AFB, Idaho, the aircraft has just killed one adversary and has fired on another with two of its AIM-120C "Slammer" AAMs. In actual combat action, the F-22 would most likely be beyond visual range of any real adversaries. If the F-22 operates as advertised, they would not even know what had fired on them, or what had hit them. *(Lockheed Martin Corporation.)*

The USAF announced in early 1996 that the 325th Fighter Wing at Tyndall AFB, Florida, will be the "schoolhouse," or training wing, for F-22 pilots once the aircraft enters USAF inventory. In this artist rendition, a Tyndall-based F-22 makes a maximum-performance takeoff with both afterburners ablaze and vortices coming off its flying surfaces. *(Lockheed Martin Corporation.)*

Rafale, and the Saab JAS 39 Gripen. In the wrong hands—and they will be sold worldwide—these could easily challenge the F-15's air superiority.

The F-22 is designed to meet all of these challenges and establish total air dominance at the outbreak of hostilities. Air dominance does not imply a battle of attrition; it means that the F-22s will shoot down all enemy opposition with little or no losses. To do this, the F-22 Raptor will not only have to be the best fighter in the world; it will have to be available in sufficient quantity to handle threats in two or more theaters of war.

Critics of the F-22 program complain that the F-15, despite its age, is still superior to aircraft of other nations. And, as General Richard E. Hawley, an experienced F-15 pilot and commander of the USAF's Air Combat Command, observed, "If you're up against a Viet Nam War–era MiG-21, you don't need an F-22."

The problem will arise when an enemy has ample numbers of aircraft equal to the F-15, and instead of a war such as in the Persian Gulf, the United States might find itself engaged in World War II style combat. Production of an adequate number of F-22s will prevent this scenario from developing, for the Raptor is expected to be 10 times as effective as the F-15, and is thus absolutely necessary to achieve immediate air dominance.

The F-22 has a remarkable combination of capabilities. Its supersonic cruise capability will get it into the target area at long range; its stealth will keep its arrival secret from the enemy. The Raptor's first-look, first-shoot, and first-kill capability will clear the skies of enemy planes at long range. If a dogfight does ensue, its thrust vectoring for superior low-

As he flies near Mount McKinley, Alaska, an F-22 pilot from the Third Wing at Elmendorf AFB enjoys the view during a training sortie. A USAF pilot said: "While the F-15 is the best all-around fighter I've ever flown and the F-16 is great fun-to-fly hot rod, I can't wait to get my hands on a '22." Note how the close-coupled stabilators on the F-22 meld with the trailing edges of the wings. *(Lockheed Martin Corporation.)*

speed agility and maneuverability, missiles, and cannons will ensure its victory. The F-22 is clearly the finest fighter in the world. The most expensive course the United States could take would be to cut expenditure on the F-22 and try to make do with F-15s. If the F-22 is procured in adequate numbers, it will preserve peace by preventing wars—no enemy will dare to take on Raptors in aerial combat.

F-22 Specifications

Primary mission	Air dominance fighter
Mission capabilities	Fighter-bomber, fighter-interceptor, high-speed photographic reconnaissance and wild weasel
User	USAF Air Combat Command
Wing area	840 sq ft
Wingspan	44 ft, 6 in (13.60 m)
Length	62 ft, 1 in (18.90 m)
Height	16 ft, 5 in (5.08 m)
Powerplant	Two augmented (afterburning) 35,000-lb thrust class (158-kiloton class) Pratt & Whitney F119-PW-100 turbofan engines with two-dimensional thrust-vectoring exhaust nozzles
Maximum speed at sea level	900 mph
Maximum speed at altitude	Mn 2.5+ (estimated)
Supercruise speed	Mn 1.5+ (estimated)
Service ceiling	65,000 ft (estimated)
Maximum rate of climb	40,000 fpm (ft/min) (estimated)
Combat range	2000 mi with internal fuel (estimated)
Maximum ferry range	5000 mi with four 600-gal (2,270-liter) externally mounted fuel tanks (estimated)
Empty weight	34,000 lb (estimated)
Gross weight	65,000 lb (estimated)
Primary armament	Four (minimum) or six (compressed-carriage) AIM-120 AMRAAMs internally, two AIM-9M (later AIM-9X) Sidewinder AAMs internally, and a single rotary-action six-barreled M-61A2 20-mm Vulcan cannon with 480 rounds of ammunition

Secondary armament	Two AIM-120 AMRAAMs internally (compressed), two AIM-9 AAMs internally, two 1000-lb class (450-kg class) GBU-32 JDAMs internally, and one M-61A2 Vulcan cannon (480 rounds)
Optional armament	Six AIM-120 AMRAAMs internally (compressed), eight AIM-120 AMRAAMs externally, two AIM-9 AAMs internally, and one M-61A2 Vulcan cannon (480 rounds)

F-22 Production

Planned F-22A Production (as of Mid-1999)

Lot number	Lot size	Calendar year of full contract award
1	2	1999 (PRTV F-22As)
2	6	2000 (IP F-22As)
3	12	2001
4	20	2002
5	30	2003
6–12	36 per year*	Yearly 2004–2010*
12	17*	2011*

*The government's System Program Officer has received guidance from the Acquisition Executive to plan for a 339-aircraft program and has passed that information on to the contractor team.

Planned EMD F-22A Production (as of Mid-1999)

LMAS production number	USAF serial number	Comment
3999	None assigned	Static structural loads test airframe
4000	None assigned	Static fatigue test airframe
4001	91-0001	First flight on 09-07-97; Paul Metz
4002	91-0002	First flight on 06-29-98; Paul Metz
4003	91-0003	First flight scheduled for mid-1999; Chuck Killberg; Block 2 avionics
4004	91-0004	First flight scheduled for February 2000; Bret Luedke; stealth testing

Planned EMD F-22A Production (as of Mid-1999) (*Continued*)

LMAS production number	USAF serial number	Comment
4005	91-0005	—
4006	91-0006	Block 3 avionics
4007	91-0007	—
4008	91-0008	—
4009	91-0009	—
4010	99-????	First of two PRTV F-22As
4011	99-????	Second PRTV F-22A
4012–4017	00-????/-????	Six initial-production F-22As
4018–4339	—	Full-production F-22As

Beddown Locations Actual operational locations have not been announced at this writing. However, at this writing, two test and training F-22s have been assigned to the 412th TW at the Air Force Flight Test Center, Edwards AFB; more will follow. A number will be assigned to the 325th Fighter Wing for F-22 pilot training at Tyndall AFB, Florida, and a number will be assigned to the Air Force Fighter Weapons School at Nellis AFB, Nevada.

F-22 Chronology

1972

JULY 27 The first example of what would become America's premier fighter, fighter-bomber, and fighter-interceptor—the McDonnell Douglas (now Boeing) F-15A Eagle—made a successful first flight at Edwards AFB. At the time, the first Eagle was to the world what the first Raptor is today: the best there is.

1976

OCTOBER The F-15 Eagle achieved initial operational capability (IOC) with the 1st Tactical Fighter Wing, 27th Tactical Fighter Squadron, at Langley AFB, Virginia.

1981

JUNE To find an eventual replacement for the F-15 Eagle, the first request for information (RFI) was issued to the industry. With this action, the Advanced Tactical Fighter (ATF) program had begun.

OCTOBER The USAF finished its evaluations of the responses to its industrywide RFI release dealing with the ATF project.

NOVEMBER The USAF formally identifies a requirement for a new air superiority fighter, the ATF, to ultimately replace the F-15 Eagle.

1983

MAY Pratt & Whitney initiates design of its PW5000, which is later designated YF119-PW-100; simultaneously, General Electric begins design of the GE37, later designated YF120-GE-100.

SEPTEMBER   The USAF awards concept definition contracts to seven aircraft manufacturers capable of producing the Advanced Tactical Fighter, or ATF. The seven aircraft manufacturers included Boeing, General Dynamics, Grumman, Lockheed, McDonnell Douglas, Northrop, and Rockwell. Simultaneously, joint advanced fighter engine (JAFE) Demonstration/Validation or Dem/Val contracts are awarded to General Electric and Pratt & Whitney.

1985

SEPTEMBER   The formal ATF Request for Proposal or RFP was issued. Pratt & Whitney fabricated the first F119 engine parts.

NOVEMBER   The USAF issues more stringent low-observables (stealth) goals for the ATF.

1986

MAY   Secretary of the Air Force Edward Aldridge announced that as part of the Packard Commission guidelines, the ATF Dem/Val program would now include prototype aircraft, engines, and a prototype avionics demonstration.

JUNE   The USAF awards contracts to Pratt & Whitney and General Electric for the ATF prototype engines, which were designated YF119-PW-100 and YF120-GE-100, respectively.

AUGUST   Lockheed, Boeing, and General Dynamics signed a Memorandum of Understanding leading to a teaming agreement on the ATF program.

SEPTEMBER   Assembly on the first YF119-PW-100 engine began. It would begin testing the following month.

OCTOBER 31   The Lockheed/Boeing/General Dynamics team is one of two teams selected to compete in the Dem/Val phase of the ATF program. The team will build two YF-22A prototypes. Simultaneously, the second of two teams—Northrop/McDonnell Douglas—were selected to build two YF-23A prototypes. Two ATF competitors, Grumman and Rockwell, were eliminated.

1987

JULY 10   The original design of the YF-22 was determined to be technically and competitively unacceptable by the Lockheed/Boeing/General Dynamics team.

JULY 13   The Lockheed-led ATF contractor team initiated new YF-22 configuration design and development.

JULY 17   Initial tests of the YF-22's avionics system are carried out on the team's Avionics Flying Laboratory (AFL) aircraft, a Boeing-owned Boeing 757 jetliner.

OCTOBER   The new configuration of the YF-22A is selected.

DECEMBER   The requirement for thrust reversers was eliminated from the ATF program.

1988

NOVEMBER 10   The long-rumored existence of a stealth fighter was officially announced during a press conference at the Pentagon. It was designated F-117A (not F-19, as had been widely rumored) and was being produced by Lockheed, which was employing some of its stealth characteristics to its YF-22A ATF prototype aircraft.

NOVEMBER 22   The premier stealth bomber, the Northrop (now Northrop Grumman) B-2A, made its first public appearance. Suddenly, low observables, or stealth technologies, were running rampant and it had become obvious that the winning ATF design would be relying heavily on this new and exciting technology.

1989

AUGUST   RFPs on the Full-Scale Development (FSD) phase of the ATF program were drafted.

OCTOBER 6   The Defense Acquisition Board approved a 6-month delay in early FSD aircraft work, thereby extending the Dem/Val phase to mid-1991.

1990

JANUARY   Final assembly of the first YF-22A prototype began at Lockheed's Palmdale, California, Site 10 facility within the U.S. Air Force Plant 42 complex.

FEBRUARY   Final assembly of the second YF-22A prototype began.

JUNE 8   Pratt & Whitney delivered the first flyable YF119 engine to Lockheed.

JUNE 17   Pratt & Whitney delivered its second flyable YF119 engine to Lockheed.

JUNE 22   The first of two Northrop/McDonnell Douglas YF-23A ATF prototype aircraft (87-0800) rolled out at Edwards AFB; its civil registration number is N231YF. It was nicknamed *Black Widow II*.

AUGUST   The second prototype YF119 engine (YF604-2) completed accelerated mission testing. The first prototype YF119 engine (YF605-1) completed flight clearance testing for the YF-22A at the Arnold Engineering and Development Center in Tennessee.

AUGUST 27   The premier YF-23A, powered by two Pratt & Whitney YF119s, completed a successful first flight at Edwards AFB; it was flown by Northrop ATF chief test pilot A. Paul Metz (now Lockheed Martin F-22 chief test pilot).

AUGUST 28   The first of two Lockheed/Boeing/General Dynamics YF-22 *Lightning II* ATF prototype aircraft (N22YF) made its public debut at Lockheed's Plant 10 in Palmdale. The first Prototype Air Vehicle or PAV-1, is powered by two General Electric YF120-GE-100 turbofan engines.

SEPTEMBER 29   The first YF-22A (N22YF), powered by two GE YF120s, made its first flight out of Palmdale, and it landed at Edwards AFB; it was piloted by Lockheed ATF chief test pilot Dave Ferguson.

OCTOBER 25   Major Mark Shackelford became the first USAF pilot to fly the YF-22A prototype. This flight also marked the first time the YF-22 was flown at supersonic speed.

OCTOBER 26   The second YF-23A (87-0801), powered by two GE YF120s, made a successful first flight at Edwards AFB; it was piloted by Northrop test pilot Jim Sandberg. It was nicknamed *Gray Ghost*.

OCTOBER 26   With the tanker aircraft being a Boeing KC-135 Stratotanker, the first aerial refueling of a YF-22 took place.

OCTOBER 29   Pratt & Whitney delivered its third flyable YF119 (a spare) to Lockheed.

OCTOBER 30   The second YF-22A Lightning II aircraft (PAV-2), powered by two P&W YF119s, made its first flight from Palmdale to Edwards AFB; it was flown by Lockheed test pilot Tom Morgenfeld.

OCTOBER 31   The USAF issued its RFP for ATF FSD and moved its FSD decision to April 1991; the ATF contractor team would then be selected.

NOVEMBER 3   As carried out with PAV-1, powered by two GE YF120s, the YF-22A's ability to supercruise, or fly at supersonic speeds without using its afterburners, was demonstrated for the first time.

NOVEMBER 14   The first YF119-powered YF-23A achieved Mn 1.43 for its highest reported supercruise speed; the second YF120-powered YF-23A's maximum achieved supercruise speed is classified but is rumored to be Mn 1.6.

NOVEMBER 15   The General Electric YF120-powered YF-22A's thrust-vectoring capability was demonstrated for the first time.

NOVEMBER 23   The Pratt & Whitney YF119-powered YF-22A (PAV-2) demonstrated its supercruise capability for the first time.

NOVEMBER 28   General Dynamics test pilot Jon Beesley (flying PAV-2) fired an unarmed AIM-9 Sidewinder heat-seeking air-to-air missile over a range at the Naval Weapons Center at China Lake, California. This was the first live missile firing in the entire ATF program.

DECEMBER 1   The Pratt & Whitney-powered YF-22A's thrust vectoring capability was demonstrated for the first time.

DECEMBER 10   Testing of the YF-22A's ability to reach high-angle-of-attack (or high-alpha) attitudes began. All the high-alpha tests were conducted with PAV-1. The YF-22A reached a reported maximum AOA of 60° degrees

DECEMBER 11   The two YF-22A prototypes were flown in formation for the first time.

DECEMBER 17   High alpha testing was completed. The YF-22A (PAV-1) attained an unprecedented 60° AOA attitude and remained in full control.

DECEMBER 20   Lockheed test pilot Tom Morgenfeld, flying PAV-2, successfully fired an unarmed AIM-120 radar-guided AMRAAM over the Pacific Missile Test Range off Port Mugu, California.

DECEMBER 28   The YF-22A's maximum Mach number (Mn 2.0+) was achieved. During the Dem/Val flight test program, PAV-1 was flown 43 times for 52.8 hours and PAV-2 was flown 31 times for 38.8 hours. In total, then, the two ATF prototypes were flown 74 times, accumulating 91.6 flying hours.

DECEMBER 31   The Lockheed/Boeing/General Dynamics team submitted its ATF FSD proposal to the USAF.

1991

JANUARY   Lockheed's F-22 program offices begin to relocate from Burbank, California, to Marietta, Georgia.

JANUARY 3   The Lockheed/Boeing/General Dynamics team made its oral summary presentation to the USAF.

APRIL 22   U.S. Air Force Secretary Dr. Donald Rice announced that, because of declining defense budgets, the total number of ATFs to be procured is now reduced from 750 to 648 aircraft.

APRIL 23   Air Force Secretary Dr. Donald Rice announced at a Pentagon briefing that the Lockheed/Boeing/General Dynamics YF-22A airplane and the Pratt & Whitney YF119-PW-100 engine combination had won the ATF competition. Dr. Rice said that the F-22/F119 combination offers "clearly better capability with lower cost, thereby providing the Air Force with a true best value." Therefore, the USAF awarded a $9.55 billion Engineering and Manufacturing Development or (EMD) contract to the Lockheed/Boeing/General Dynamics team.

JUNE   The number one YF-22A prototype was flown aboard a Lockheed C-5 Galaxy to Andrews AFB, Maryland, to participate in the USAF's "Stealth Week," an informal exhibition for Congress and the media. The YF-22A was displayed with a Lockheed F-117A Nighthawk stealth fighter, an Advanced Cruise Missile, and a Northrop B-2A Spirit stealth bomber.

JUNE 23   The number one YF-22A was flown to Marietta aboard a C-5. The airplane, never to be flown again, was then put to use as an engineering mockup.

AUGUST 2   The USAF awarded the Lockheed/Boeing/General Dynamics team a $9.55 billion contract to begin EMD (formerly FSD) of the F-22. Eleven flyable (nine single-seat F-22As and two tandem-seat F-22Bs) aircraft and one static test airframe and one fatigue test airframe would be built under this particular contract. Pratt & Whitney, under a separate $1.375 billion contract for engine development, would build 33 flightworthy F119-PW-100 turbofan engines; the contracts were signed the next day. At this time it was announced that the first EMD aircraft would fly in mid-1996 (then May 1997 but September 1997 actual), the first production aircraft in mid 1999, and IOC in 2003 (2005 actual).

SEPTEMBER   The number two YF-22A prototype was trucked from Edwards AFB to Palmdale for a planned layup and the installation of test equipment. It was trucked back to Edwards in mid-October.

OCTOBER 30   The number two YF-22A (N22YX) resumed flight testing at Edwards AFB as Lockheed test pilot Tom Morgenfeld made a 1.6-hour sortie.

NOVEMBER 13   Ground was broken in Marietta for the L-22 building, the new office home of the F-22 program. A three-story, 150,000-sq-ft building was scheduled for completion in late-1992. During construction, the plans were revised to make L-22 a four-story building; it was scheduled for occupancy in spring, 1993; actual occupancy began on April 26, 1993.

DECEMBER 16   The external design of the F-22 was frozen during the Air vehicle requirements/design review update. This allowed wind-tunnel and radar cross-section (RCS) models to be built, the internal design to be completed, and eventually prepare tooling for manufacturing the aircraft.

1992

JANUARY 10   With 53.0 hours of total flight time accumulated during Dem/Val and the postcontract award flight-test phase, the F119-powered YF-22A surpassed the number of hours flown by PAV-1 (52.8) during Dem/Val.

JANUARY 21   With 44 flights completed during the two flight test phases, the number of sorties flown in PAV-2 surpassed the total flown in PAV-1 (43) during Dem/Val.

APRIL 7   With 40.3 hours flown, PAV-2 had flown more hours in the postcontract award flight-test phase than it did during Dem/Val (38.8).

APRIL 11   Air Force Lt. Col. Jay Jabour made the 32nd test sortie in PAV-2 since the resumption of flight test in October 1991. The second YF-22A had flown more times during this phase than it did in Dem/Val (31).

APRIL 25   Returning to Edwards AFB after a test flight, the second YF-22A experienced a series of pitch oscillations at about 40 ft above the runway. With landing gear retracted, the aircraft hit the runway, slid about 800 ft, and caught fire. Although no longer flightworthy, the external damage was later repaired, and it was flown aboard a C-5 to the Rome Air Development Center at Griffiss AFB, New York, where it was to undergo a series of antenna tests. In all, PAV-2 had been flown 70 times for a total of 100.4 hours.

JUNE   Critical design reviews (CDRs) are held for all F119 EMD test engine components. These thorough reviews of the engine mark completion of the detailed design phase of the program and ensure that the F119 was ready to proceed into fabrication and assembly.

JUNE 4   The F-22's design review update (DRU) was completed.

DECEMBER 17   The first EMD F119 engine goes to test.

1993

JANUARY   As the result of a fiscal year 1993 funding shortfall due to cost increases and Congressional budget cuts, the F-22 EMD program schedule was rephased. Key events in the development process would now occur anywhere from 6 to 18 months later than originally scheduled. The rephasing also reduced the number of aircraft to be built during EMD from 11 to 9 (which still included two F-22B tandem-seat fighter trainers); thus, 7 single-seat, and 2 tandem-seat aircraft. The F119 engine program was also rephased, and Pratt & Whitney would now build only 27 (rather than 33) flightworthy EMD engines.

MARCH 1   Lockheed Corporation completed the acquisition of General Dynamics' Fort Worth Division, Texas. That $1.5 billion purchase (which was announced the previous December) increased Lockheed's majority share of the F-22 program from 35 to 67.5 percent. Boeing's 32.5 percent share of the program remains unchanged.

APRIL 26   Occupancy of the L-22 building begins. This four-story, 200,000-sq-ft facility is home to more than 900 people working on the F-22 program at Marietta. The building also has a 251-person conference center.

APRIL 30   The F-22 air vehicle preliminary design review (PDR) was completed. This PDR completed the third and final phase of preliminary design work on the F-22. This was also the first major event held in the new L-22 building in Marietta.

DECEMBER 8   Albert Ferara, a milling machine operator at Boeing Defense and Space Group, Kent, Washington, began fabrication of the first part of the first flyable EMD F-22A. The part, made of titanium, is one of eight forward boom keelson panels that would make up one section of the F-22's aft fuselage section.

1994

FEBRUARY 10   As one result of the continuing downsizing of the U.S. military forces, the USAF announced that the number of production F-22s to be procured had been reduced from 648 to 442, reduced from 750 to 648 earlier.

MARCH 4   It was announced that the F-22 Air Force/industry design team had identified some shortfalls in the aircraft's radar cross-section (RCS) signature. The shortfalls, which were identified through a new computer modeling technique, were to be addressed by late spring through an intensive effort. The fixes involved the reduction in number of drain holes on the bottom of the aircraft and combining access panels.

OCTOBER 6   Charles Wilkey, a milling machine operator at LASC in Marietta, began fabrication of the first part LASC built for the first flyable F-22. The aluminum part was for an engine air inlet duct frame segment.

NOVEMBER   Acquisition of P&W F119 flight-test engine long-lead-time hardware was initiated.

DECEMBER 9   Secretary of Defense William Perry, often referred to as the "father of stealth," announced $8 billion in budget changes to seven Department of Defense modernization programs. These included a 10 percent reduction in the Fiscal Year 1996 research and development funding for the F-22. This cut necessitated a third rephase of the F-22 program.

DECEMBER   Lockheed Fort Worth Company, in Texas, began fabrication of the first graphite composite parts for the first midfuselage section of the first flyable F-22.

1995

FEBRUARY 24   The USAF approved the final design of the F-22A. The formal portion of the F-22 air vehicle critical design review (CDR) was completed. This review of the F-22 air vehicle marked completion of the detailed design phase of the program and ensured that the F-22 was ready to proceed into fabrication and assembly.

MARCH 15   Lockheed Corporation and Martin Marietta completed their "merger of equals." The combined enterprise was named Lockheed Martin Corporation. Lockheed Aeronautical Systems Company (LASC) became Lockheed Martin Aeronautical Systems (LMAS), and Lockheed Fort Worth Company (LFWC) became Lockheed Martin Tactical Aircraft Systems (LMTAS).

APRIL 20   The USAF awarded the Lockheed Martin/Boeing team a $9.5 million, 24-month study contract to explore derivatives to the F-22 aircraft. Pratt & Whitney was awarded a separate $500,000 contract to explore improved F119 engine performance. The USAF later curtailed this study.

JUNE 27   Assembly of the first flyable F-22 began as workers loaded the first midfuselage bulkhead into an assembly fixture at LMTAS in Fort Worth. This milestone was achieved ahead of schedule.

JULY   Pratt & Whitney's redesigned F119 turbine demonstrated improved fuel efficiency and elimination of turbine blade vibratory stress.

JULY 24   Wind tunnel testing of the F-22's configuration was completed. Twenty-three models were tested in 14 facilities throughout the United States and in Germany during the 16,930-hour wind tunnel program that began in 1991.

OCTOBER 4   Assembly of the first flyable F-22 began at Boeing Military Airplanes as workers loaded parts for the aft fuselage section into an assembly fixture.

NOVEMBER 2   Assembly of the first flyable F-22 began at LMAS in Marietta as workers loaded parts of the nose landing gear wheel well into an assembly fixture.

1996

JANUARY 17   Boeing began assembly of the first shipset of wings for the first flyable F-22. The left, or port, wing was started first.

FEBRUARY   Tests of the F-22's flight control laws began in the Variable Stability In-flight Simulator Aircraft (VISTA), a highly-modified, one-of-a-kind Lockheed Martin F-16D Fighting Falcon (86-0048) that, through a sophisticated control system, emulates the flying characteristics of another type of aircraft while in flight. These tests, which took place over upstate New York, were flown in two sessions and were completed in May 1996.

MAY 6   Pratt & Whitney began assembly of the first flight test F119 engine at its Middletown, Connecticut, facility.

JULY 9   Pratt & Whitney conducted a "Last Bolt" ceremony at Middletown to mark the completion of the first flight-test F119 engine.

JULY 10   The airframe team received formal notification from the USAF that deferred the requirement for design and development of the two-seat F-22B fighter trainer. The two planned EMD F-22Bs were replaced by two single-seat F-22As, so all nine EMD F-22s would now be single-seat aircraft.

AUGUST 29 LMTAS in Fort Worth held a triceremony to commemorate the completion of the midfuselage section for the first flyable F-22, mating of the midfuselage for F-22 number 2, and loading the first midfuselage assembly for F-22 number 3.

SEPTEMBER 6 The midfuselage for the first flyable F-22 (ship 1) arrived in Marietta after a 4-day truck trip from LMTAS in Fort Worth. Shortly thereafter, the mating of the forward fuselage to the midfuselage sections began.

SEPTEMBER 24 Pratt & Whitney announced that the first flight test F119 engine had been delivered to the USAF. It was then taken to Arnold AFB, Tennessee, for testing, after which it was to be delivered to LMAS in Marietta.

OCTOBER 1 Northrop Grumman announced that the first developmental AN/APG-77, the electronically steered, active element, phased-array radar unit to be used in the F-22, began system-level integration and test. The AN/APG-77 radar system had been developed by Westinghouse, and was later purchased by Northrop Grumman Corporation.

OCTOBER 8 The first of two flight-test EMD F119 engines was delivered via truck to LMAS in Marietta.

OCTOBER 16 The aft fuselage section for the first flyable F-22 arrived in Marietta, and mating operations began. It was delivered from Boeing's Seattle via C-5 Galaxy.

OCTOBER 27 The completed fuselage for the first F-22 was lifted from the body mate tool to the wing mate tool.

NOVEMBER 9 The wings for the first F-22 arrived from Boeing's Seattle facility to Marietta, and mate operations began 2 days later.

DECEMBER Electrical power was applied to the first F-22 for the first time.

1997

JANUARY 16 The first P&W F119 engine was test-fitted into the first EMD F-22A.

JANUARY 21 The F-22A's left vertical stabilizer was installed.

FEBRUARY 6 The F-22A's right vertical stabilizer was installed.

FEBRUARY 17 F119 engine endurance testing was completed.

MARCH 6 The first F-22A, nearly complete, was towed from its final assembly area in LMAS' B-1 building to the newly constructed B-22 engine noise attenuation facility—called a "hush house," where it underwent fueling operations and engine runs.

MARCH 31 The P&W F119-PW-100 engine was granted initial flight release (IFR) status.

APRIL 9 The premier EMD F-22A was publicly unveiled in ceremonies at LMAS in Marietta. During the ceremony, the fighter was christened with its official name: *Raptor.*

MAY The first flight of the first Raptor was to occur. Moderate problems, including landing gear and wheel braking difficulties, delayed the first flight for 4 months.

MAY 15 Quadrennial Defense Review Report was released. It reduced the F-22 overall production quantity from 438 to 339.

JULY 31 The first F-22A Raptor's F119-PW-100 engines were run at full afterburner (maximum power) for the first time. Tied down, the engines were brought up to full afterburner one at a time.

SEPTEMBER The first F-22A Raptor underwent a series of low-, medium-, and high-speed taxi tests to check nose wheel steering, brakes, and so on.

SEPTEMBER 7   Lockheed Martin F-22A chief test pilot A. Paul Metz successfully completes the maiden flight of the first EMD F-22A from Marietta, Georgia; the flight lasted 58 minutes.

SEPTEMBER 14   Lockheed Martin F-22A test pilot Jon Beesley completed the second flight of F-22A number 1. The flight, cut short because of a telemetry glitch, lasted about 35 minutes.

NOVEMBER 21   The first AN/APG-77 radar test flight took place aboard the 757 FTB (formerly AF2) aircraft.

1998

FEBRUARY 5   The first F-22A Raptor (4001) was delivered to Edwards AFB, California, via a C-5 Galaxy.

FEBRUARY 10   The second of nine EMD F-22A Raptor aircraft (4002) was rolled out of the 3.5 million-sq-ft main assembly B-1 building in Marietta.

MARCH   The final production readiness review (PRR) for the F119 engine took place at P&W's facility in West Palm Beach, Florida; subsequent to the PRR, the F119's full flight release was granted.

APRIL   The number 1 YF-22 prototype, painted and marked like the P&W YF119-powered YF-22 prototype, was enshrined at the U.S. Air Museum at Wright-Patterson AFB, Ohio.

MAY 17   The first F-22A Raptor aircraft made its first flight at Edwards AFB. The flight lasted 1 hour and 20 minutes, and its general speed was at or below 350 knots (525 mph). It was Raptor 01's third flight.

JUNE   Boeing completed and delivered its third aft fuselage section 3 weeks ahead of its revised schedule. Once attached to the rest of the aircraft, it will never fly, for this section was built for the static structural loads airframe.

JUNE   The USAF granted Lockheed Martin and Boeing 87 percent of a $44 million incentive for work performed from October 1997 to March 1998. It also recognized the F-22 team with a special 100 percent award fee—$20 million—for an F-22 production-affordability analysis conducted in 1998 by the contractors. The total amount was about $58 million (two-thirds to Lockheed Martin Corporation, one-third to The Boeing Company).

JUNE 29   The second F-22A Raptor (LMAS 4002) made its first flight out of Dobbins Air Reserve Base; Paul Metz was the pilot.

JULY 1   Raptor 02 made its second flight at Dobbins ARB.

JULY 9   Raptor 01 made its 12th flight; first F-22 flight by Chuck Killberg, chief F-22 test pilot for Boeing.

JULY 10   Raptor 01 made its 13th flight; Chuck Killberg was the pilot.

JULY 10   Lockheed Martin announced that the USAF had awarded the Lockheed Martin/Boeing F-22 team two contracts totaling up to $70.7 million for advance procurement and program support for two F-22A production representative test vehicles (PRTVs). These contracts, valued at up to $2.1 billion, include options for the two PRTVs and the six initial production (IP) IP F-22As. The two PRTVs and the six IP F-22As have been assigned LMAS production numbers 4010–4017. At this writing, the USAF plans to buy the two PRTV aircraft and 12 production lots totaling 339 F-22 aircraft, at an estimated cost of $34.7 billion in fiscal year 1998 (FY 98) dollars. FY 98 began on October 1, 1997 and ended on October 31, 1998.

JULY 30 Lockheed Martin Tactical Aircraft Systems in Fort Worth, Texas, completed a series of AIM-9 and AIM-120 weapons fit tests on an F-22A.

AUGUST 23 Raptor 02 flew for 4.6 hours, the longest sortie to date, and air-refueled two times. This duration sortie was highly successful and served as a dress rehearsal for the aircraft's upcoming ferry flight to Edwards AFB.

AUGUST 26 Raptor 02 (AF 91-0002) flew from Dobbins ARB to Edwards AFB in a 4-hour, 35-minute nonstop flight. The flight included two aerial refuelings by two Boeing KC-135 Stratotankers.

AUGUST 31 Raptors 01 and 02 completed 59.4 flying hours in 38 flights.

SEPTEMBER F-22 Integrated avionics flight testing at Boeing with the 757 FTB began.

SEPTEMBER While flying at high altitudes and throttle settings, Raptor 02 experienced enough engine (left) vibration to prematurely terminate a flight test. Subsequently, the left engine was removed, and after a thorough inspection, it was found that it had been improperly installed. The engine was not at fault.

SEPTEMBER 1 Raptor 01 reached an angle of attack or (AOA) of 16° at Edwards AFB.

SEPTEMBER 7 The first anniversary of the first flight of the premier F-22A Raptor was celebrated by the USAF, ACC, Lockheed Martin/Boeing, Pratt & Whitney, and numerous other F-22 program participants. At this time, the aircraft had achieved Mn 0.95 and an altitude of 40,000 ft.

SEPTEMBER 21 Lockheed Martin Tactical Aircraft Systems delivered the fifth EMD F-22A midfuselage section 2 weeks ahead of schedule. This midfuselage section will be used for the second nonflying F-22 (LMAS serial no. 4000). It is one of 11 midfuselages to be built during the EMD phase of the program by LMTAS' Fort Worth, Texas facility. The midfuselage section for the first of two nonflying F-22s (LMAS serial no. 3999) was delivered in July 1998.

OCTOBER 12 The first EMD F-22A discovered supersonic flight for the first time. Piloted by Lockheed Martin test pilot Jon Beesley, Raptor 01 hit Mn 1.1 during a nearly three-hour flight at Edwards AFB.

NOVEMBER 1 To date, Raptor 01 had flown 29 sorties and 40.2 hours and Raptor 02 had flown 11 sorties and 21.2 hours for a grand total of 40 sorties and 61.4 hours. These two aircraft were scheduled to achieve 183 total flight hours on or before December 31, 1998. At this time, Raptor 03 (4003) is scheduled to arrive at Edwards in March 2000; first deliveries to operational units is to begin in 2002, and IOC is slated for November 2004.

NOVEMBER 23 The two flying Raptors achieved an earlier announced goal of 183 flying hours, flights above 40,000 ft, an AOA exceeding 18°, and aerial refuelings. Flying some 122 total flight hours between them since November 1, the two 412th Flight Test Squadron F-22As accumulated a grand total of 183 flight hours to meet the criteria for long-lead funding. At this time, the development, test, and evaluation (DT&E) is scheduled to end in 2002 with the initiation of dedicated initial operational test and evaluation (IOT&E) to follow. As of today, F-22 pilots at the Combined Test Force, Edwards Air Force Base, Calif., have logged 184.4 hours in the program's two current, flight-test F-22s, surpassing the Congressional mandate. The first F-22, Raptor 01, has flown 45 sorties and 79 flight hours, including 4.42 hours of supersonic flight. Raptor 02, the second off the assembly line, has flown 41 sorties and 105.4 flight hours.

Future Milestones (projected)

1999

JANUARY 1   Envelope expansion to higher supersonic flight and 20° AOA was met by Raptors 01 and 02 by this date.

MIDYEAR   The USAF's Low-Rate Initial Production (LRIP) contract for the F-22A is to be awarded. This Lot 1 production contract stipulates that two aircraft be delivered in late 2001 and early 2002.

MIDYEAR   The first flight of EMD F-22A number 3 (Raptor 03) is to take place by this time; Chuck Killberg is to be the pilot.

SEPTEMBER 30   The last of 27 EMD P&W F119 flight test engines is scheduled to be delivered to LMAS.

LATE   The first flight of F-22 number 4 (Raptor 04) is scheduled to take place with Bret Luedke as the pilot. It is the first Raptor to have a completely operational avionics suite.

2000

EARLY   The USAF is scheduled to award the Lot 2 production contract. These six F-22As are to be delivered in 2002.

FEBRUARY   The fourth EMD F-22, Raptor 04, is rescheduled to make its first flight at Dobbins ARB with Bret Luedke at the controls; this flight was delayed from late 1999.

JUNE   Raptor 04 (4004) is to begin flight tests with Block 3S avionics software.

2001

EARLY   The USAF is scheduled to award the Lot 3 production contract. These 12 F-22As are to be delivered in 2003.

MIDYEAR   The last of nine F-22s to be built during the EMD phase of the Raptor program is scheduled to be delivered to the USAF.

2002

EARLY   The contractor portion of the EMD phase of the F-22 program is scheduled to be completed.

EARLY   The USAF is scheduled to award the Lot 4 production contract. These 20 F-22As are to be delivered starting in late 2003 and running through 2004.

MIDYEAR   First F-22 deliveries to user squadrons are to begin.

2003

EARLY   The USAF's dedicated IOT&E program is scheduled to be completed, thus officially ending the EMD phase of the F-22 program.

EARLY   The USAF is scheduled to award the Lot 5 production contract. These 30 F-22As are to be delivered starting in late 2004 and running through 2005.

2004

EARLY   The high-rate production decision for the F-22 is expected to be made by the USAF. This Lot 6 contract will cover 48 aircraft. These F-22s will be delivered in late 2005 and 2006.

LATE   The F-22A Raptor was scheduled to enter operational service, meeting its initial operational capability (IOC).

2005

EARLY   The F-22A is expected to enter operational service, delayed from late 2004.

2007

SEPTEMBER 7   The 10th anniversary of Raptor 01's first flight is to be celebrated.

2011

LATE   The last of 339 F-22As currently planned for USAF procurement will be delivered. Breakdown is as follows: nine EMD F-22As, two PRTV F-22As, six IP F-22As, and 322 FSP F-22As.

2022

SEPTEMBER 7   The 25th anniversary of Raptor 01's first flight.

Books

Goodall, James C. 1992. *America's Stealth Fighters and Bombers: B-2, F-117, YF-22, and YF-23.* Osceola, WI: Motorbooks International Publishers and Wholesalers.

Miller, Jay. 1993. *Lockheed's Skunk Works: The First Fifty Years.* Arlington, TX: Aerofax, Inc.

Pace, Steve. 1991. *X-Fighters: USAF Experimental and Prototype Jet Fighters, XP-59A to YF-23A.* Osceola, WI: Motorbooks International Publishers and Wholesalers.

———. 1992. *Lockheed Skunk Works.* Osceola, WI: Motorbooks International Publishers and Wholesalers.

———. 1994. *Edwards Air Force Base: Experimental Flight Test Center.* Osceola, WI: Motorbooks International Publishers and Wholesalers.

———. 1995. *X-Planes at Edwards.* Osceola, WI: Motorbooks International Publishers and Wholesalers.

Rich, Ben R., and Leo Janos. 1994. *Skunk Works.* New York: Little, Brown and Company.

Sweetman, Bill. 1998. *F-22 Raptor.* Osceola, WI: Motorbooks International Publishers and Wholesalers.

Magazine Articles

Air Force Magazine. Air Force Association. Monthly; various issues from January 1990 to date.

Aviation Week and Space Technology Magazine. The McGraw-Hill Companies. Weekly; various issues from July 1988 to date.

Dorr, Robert F. Computer Technology and the F-22 Fighter. *The Year In Computing 1997–1998,* pp. 28–30, 32, 34, 36, 38–40.

Flight International Magazine. Reed Business Information, Ltd. Weekly; various issues from September 1991 to date.

Hehs, Eric. 1998. F-22 Design Evolution Part I: The Story behind the Raptor's Genesis. *Code One,* April, pp. 2–17.

Hehs, Eric. 1998. F-22 Design Evolution Part II: From Teaming to a Winning Team. *Code One,* October, pp. 24–41.

Pace, Steve. 1987. Fighter on the Fringe: The Air Force's New Advanced Tactical Fighter, the ATF, Marvel of the Future! *Wings,* April, pp. 20–37 and 55.

Reports and Papers

Lockheed Martin Aeronautical Systems Communications Office. 1997. *F-22 Raptor Media Guide* (1st ed.). Marietta, GA.

ACC	Air Combat Command*
ACES II	Advanced Concept Ejection Seat II[†]
ACF	Air Combat Fighter
ADF	Air Dominance Fighter
AFB	Air Force Base
AFFTC	Air Force Flight Test Center
AFFTC/HO	Air Force Flight Test Center History Office
AFMC	Air Force Materiel Command[‡]
AFOTEC	Air Force Operational Test and Evaluation Center
AGM	Air-to-Ground Missile
AIM	Airborne Intercept Missile[§]
AMAD	Airframe Mounted Accessory Drive
AMRAAM	Advanced Medium-Range Air-to-Air Missile[¶]
AN	Army and Navy
APU	Auxiliary Power Unit
ARB	Air Reserve Base
ARPA	Advanced Research Projects Agency
ASD	Aeronautical Systems Division
ASP	Air Superiority Fighter

*Activated June 1, 1992; combines the former Strategic Air Command and Tactical Air Command.

[†]Standard emergency ejection seat used in bomber and fighter aircraft, including the F-22.

[‡]Formerly Air Force Systems Command or (AFSC).

[§]The AIM-9M Sidewinder as currently used by the F-22.

[¶]The AIM-120C "Slammer" as currently used by the F-22.

ATF	Advanced Tactical Fighter
BMI	Bismaleimide
BVR	Beyond Visual Range
CEP	Circular Error Probable
CNI	Communication-Navigation-Identification
CPS	Composite Pivot Shaft
CTF	Combined Test Force
DARPA	Defense Advanced Research Projects Agency
Dem/Val	Demonstration and Validation
DoD	Department of Defense
EAFB	Edwards Air Force Base
ECS	Environmental Control System
EMD	Engineering and Manufacturing Development
EW	Electronic Warfare
FADEC	Full-Authority Digital Electronic Engine Control
FSD	Full Scale Development
FSP	Full Scale Production
FTB	Flying Test Bed
FT&E	Flight-Test and Evaluation
FTRWG	Flight Test Requirements Working Group
FX	Fighter-Experimental
GBU	Guided Bomb Unit
GE	General Electric
HIP	Hot Isostatic Pressed
HUD	Head-Up Display
ICNAI	Integrated Communications-Navigation-Identification Avionics
INEWS	Integrated Electronic Warfare System
IOC	Initial Operational Capability
IOT&E	Initial Operational Test and Evaluation
IP	Initial Production
IPT	Integrated Product Team
IR	Infrared
JAFE	Joint Advanced Fighter Engine
JDAM	Joint Direct Attack Munition
JSF	Joint Strike Fighter
KIAS	Knots Indicated Air Speed
KTAS	Knots True Air Speed
LMAS	Lockheed Martin Aeronautical Systems
LMTAS	Lockheed Martin Tactical Aircraft Systems
LO	Low-Observable
LWF	Light Weight Fighter
MiG	Mikoyan Gurevich
Mn	Mach number
MOSARC	Milestone One System Acquisition Review Council
NADF	Navy Air Dominance Fighter

NATF	Navy Advanced Tactical Fighter
NATO	North Atlantic Treaty Organization
P	Pursuit*
PRTV	Production Representative Test Vehicle
P&W	Pratt and Whitney
RAM	Radar-Absorbing Material
RAS	Radar-Absorbing Structure
RCS	Radar Cross Section
RFI	Request for Information
RFP	Request for Proposal
SLAM ER	Standoff Land Attack Missile, Expanded Response
SPO	System Program Office
STOL	Short Takeoff and Landing
Su	Sukhoi
TAC	Tactical Air Command
USAF	U.S. Air Force
VHF	Very High Frequency
VHSIC	Very High-Speed Integrated Circuits
VISTA	Variable In-flight Stability Test Aircraft
WS	Weapon System
YF	Service Test Fighter/Service Test Turbofan Engine

*The P prefix was used to the late 1940s to denote USAF fighter-type aircraft; the P for *pursuit* prefix was changed to F for *fighter* in June 1948.

Steve Pace is a veteran aviation journalist and author who has written 17 books on a wide range of military aircraft and related topics. He lives in Tacoma, Washington.